Serena Leigh wurde 1997 in Japan als Tochter einer persischen Mutter und eines niederländischen Vaters geboren. Mit sechs Jahren zog sie nach Deutschland. Sie besuchte ein Gymnasium in Frankfurt. Ihr erstes Werk „Manipulation" publizierte sie im Jahr 2016. Danach folgte „sie.". Nun ist „Hazel & Ich" ein Eintrag in lyrischer Form.

Für uns.

© 2019 Serena Leigh

Auflage (2019)
Autorenbild: Sarah Hebenstreit
Titelbild: luizclas

Verlag und Druck: tredition GmbH
Halenreie 40-44, 22359 Hamburg

ISBN Paperback: 978-3-7497-2652-3
ISBN Hardcover: 978-3-7497-2653-0
ISBN e-Book: 978-3-7497-2654-7

Bibliografische Information der Deutschen Nationalbibliothek:
Die Deutsche Nationalbibliothek verzeichnet diese Publikation in der
Deutschen Nationalbibliografie; detaillierte bibliografische Daten sind im
Internet über http://dnb.d-nb.de abrufbar.

Serena Leigh

Hazel & Ich

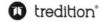

Grüne Augen, braunes Haar.

Und dort stand ich da,

Etwas schüchtern, etwas neugierig.

So war es auf dem ersten Blick.

Im neuen Büro, ich, ein neues Gesicht.

Ich freute mich immer wieder auf dich.

Nicht viel zu sagen,

Doch sehr verlegen,

War ich rot?

18. Oktober 2018

Mein Geburtstagskuchen vor mir.

Ja, du darfst dir eines nehmen.

Hatten wir Augenkontakt?

Ich glaube nicht.

Nehme mich wahr.

Ich warte auf dich.

25. Oktober 2018

Wir mailen uns selten.

An dem Tag hast du an mich gedacht.

Du fragtest: „Soll ich dir helfen?"

Ich war dir dankbar.

Ich konnte nämlich nicht viel reden.

08. November 2018

Ausgesperrt draußen im Kalten.

Ich sehe dich auf deinem Rad.

Öffnest die Tür und so fängt der Tag an.

Du bist aufmerksam.

Ich bin noch zurückhaltend.

09. November 2018

Meeting mit allen in einem Raum

Nur für paar Sekunden blickst du zu mir.

Ich rufe dich an, du erwähnst meinen Namen.

Ich lache verlegen.

Ich sage dann deinen.

11. November 2018

Stalking?

Kann man nicht so nennen.

Ich google dich.

Finde ich etwas?

Nada.

Tagein und tagaus.

Die Arbeit geht schleppend voran.

Dich sehe ich heute nicht.

Nächste Woche hast du schon Urlaub.

Ob du eine „sie" hast…?

Ich möchte ihn gerne kennen lernen.

Eine Kollegin spricht ihn an.

Sie haben des Öfteren innige Gespräche.

„Sie" hieß Hazel.

Ich beobachte die beiden manchmal mehr, manchmal weniger.

Ich würde wissen wollen, ob auch ich eine Chance hätte.

Sie schlank, brünett und Rehaugen.

Wollte ich auch mir ihr befreundet sein?

Ich halte lieber Abstand.

28. November 2018

Ich konzentriere mich bei der Arbeit.

Kichernde Geräusche im Hintergrund, die ich nicht abschalten kann.

Er ist wirklich attraktiv, doch ich noch viel zu schüchtern.

Hazel sollte mich nicht stören.

Doch alles, was ich sehe, kann ich auch nur hören.

30. November 2018

Er ist tiefsinnig.

So waren ein paar unserer Gespräche

Mehr sollte auch ich nicht erfahren.

Sehr verschlossen, sehr gedankenvoll.

Schmerzhaft zu wissen, dass er mit Hazel zu tun hatte,

nicht mit mir.

Sollte ich in die Quere kommen?

Das bleibt nur ein Wunschgedanke.

03. Dezember 2018

Hazel ist ein gentiles Mädchen.

Wir helfen uns gegenseitig.

Sie redet viel über ihn, aber in etwas Festem ist sie schon.

Ob das wichtig sei?

Ob das richtig sei?

Ich verstehe die Neugier, dennoch kann das zum Verhängnis werden.

06. Dezember 2018

Er redet mit mir und schenkt mir die Aufmerksamkeit.

Hazel blickt zu mir und ich höre auf.

Ich will denen nicht im Weg stehen.

Ich spreche ihn an.

Ich halte mich zurück.

Es ist kein schönes Gefühl, den Neid in sich zu tragen,

aber für jemanden sich das Glück zu wünschen.

So bleibe ich loyal zu ihr.

23. Dezember 2018

Ich werfe mich in die Arbeit.

Ich schalte alles aus.

Ich akzeptierte Hazels Wunsch.

Zugucken, wie sie turteln.

Ich bin eine faire Person.

Haben sie meinen Segen?

Hazels „festes Er" wäre sicher dagegen.

11. Januar 2019

Es ist Januar und die Zeit friert ein.

Hazel und er sind sich näher als man darf.

Stört es mich?

Ich weiß es nicht.

Ein Platz zum Konzentrieren war die Arbeit nicht mehr.

Ich bin wütend, aber laut aussprechen kann ich es nicht.

Ich wünschte, ich wäre nicht in der Mitte.

14. Januar 2019

Merkwürdig ist die Luft.

Du bist nicht hier, ich weiß nicht was du tust.

Ich kann nicht hinein schauen.

Es liegt nicht in meiner Hand, was du tust.

Ich bin kein Kontroll-Freak.

Im Büro ist es totenstill.

Lass mich in deine Welt rein!

Deine Welt, deine Gedanken, deine Schwächen, das ist
es, was wirklich will.

Ich komme zu deinem Tisch.

Ich stottere, wenn ich dich seh.

Stelle mich nicht bloß da!

Hazel richtet die Augen auf mich.

Wir werden beobachtet.

Ich beruhige mich.

Ich fasse mich.

Wir sind doch nur Kollegen.

Wir sind doch nur Kollegen.

Wir sind doch nur Kollegen?

28. Januar 2019

Du redest mit mir mit deinen Blicken.

Sollte ich das als Signal wahrnehmen?

Wir sind allein, du kommst mir näher.

Mir ist unwohl, ich spüre ihre Präsenz.

Die Präsenz von Hazel.

Sie hält mich ab, den Schritt zu wagen.

Wir versammeln uns und wollen die Nacht durchmachen.

Hazel weiß, sie wird ihm näher kommen.

Nur für eine Sekunde schaue ich weg, sie, umschlungen in seinen Armen.

Was fühle ich in mir?

Ist es Wut? Nein.

Ist es Freude? Nein.

Trauer für den Dritten, ja, das war es.

Die Nacht endete mit schlechten Entscheidungen.

Ich hielt sie nicht ab.

Er ging mit Hazel nach Hause.

Hazel warf mir den Blick zu und ich fühlte mich perplex.

Hazel ist alt genug.

Sie würde wissen.

Nur die jugendliche Aktion war reiner Unfug.

03. Februar 2019

An den Morgen danach, daran denkt keiner.

Wir wachen auf mit dem feinsten Kater.

Sie guckt sich im Spiegel an.

Bereuen kann sie nichts.

Hazel lässt alles Revue passieren.

Ihr „festes Er" kann sie jedoch nicht verlieren.

Traurig sollte ich nicht sein.

Ich war nie mit ihm wirklich allein.

Sie spielte immer eine große Rolle.

Ob sie das so wollte?

Dagegen anzukämpfen sollte ich nicht machen.

Ich sehe zu, wie sie eine dritte Person zum Weinen

brachten.

Die Person war nicht ich, sondern Hazels „festes Er".

Lustig zu beobachten war das nicht mehr.

15. Februar 2019

Ich rede mit Hazel, um Klarheit zu schaffen.

Sie sollte ihre Finger von ihm lassen.

Hazels „festes Er" sollte nicht zu Schaden kommen.

Ob sie das versteht?

Ihre Neugier ist mehr als zuvor erregt.

Feuer und Flamme sind die beiden.

Wie ein ungewolltes Stück, so stehe ich zwischen dem
Leiden.

Hazels „festes Er" sieht keinen Ausweg.

Somit beschließt er den Ausstieg.

Ihr Willen für ihre neue Liebe, sei sie nur temporär

Sie kämpft nicht um ihre Beziehung.

Den Liebenden zu verletzen, das tut man nicht primär.

04. März 2019

Jetzt sind sie allein.

Sie ließen alles hinter sich.

Nur die Trauer des Dritten nahmen sie mit.

Die Trauer, die sie nicht los lassen konnten.

Ich war nicht sauer auf die beiden, nur der Respekt gegenüber ihm verflog irgendwohin.

War es das wert? Ich verstand noch nicht den Sinn.

Verstehen kann ich es nicht.

Der innere Richter machte es mir schwer.

08. März 2019

Mal ist er da, mal verschwindet er für eine Weile.

Zuverlässig ist er nicht.

Das wusste sie von Anfang an.

Gewöhnen konnte sie sich nicht.

Mysteriös und unscheinbar, so war er.

An einen Ort binden ließ er sich nicht.

War Hazel darauf vorbereitet?

13. März 2019

Ich sah es ihr an.

Ein Blick des Verlustes?

Sie wollte eine Bestätigung ihres Beschlusses.

Ihre Gefühle konnte man nicht bändigen.

Die Antwort von mir wollte ich nicht aushändigen.

19. März 2019

So also fühlt es sich an, der Werther zu sein.

Drang, den Sturm der Gefühle zu unterdrücken.

Es war eine Sucht.

Gesund war es nicht, dennoch besser als die beiden zu verlieren.

Doch es gab eine Flucht?

20. März 2019

Hazel war Hals über Kopf für ihn.

Er jedoch verlor den Appetit.

Den Appetit der gegenseitigen Neugier.

So war es aus der Sicht von mir.

Er bekam kalte Füße vor den Bedingungen.

Er schrieb ihr:

„Ich brauche neue Luft. Luft, die du mir nicht geben

kannst. Es war eine Begegnung, die ich nicht unversucht

lassen wollte."

21. März 2019

Er ließ Hazel sprachlos.

Ihr blieb nur die Erinnerung, die sie gemeinsam hatten.

Sie fiel mir in die Arme und verdrückte eine Träne.

In meiner Hand dieses Büchlein.

Sie bedankt sich für die Worte.

Sie schließt ihre Augen für eine Weile.

Es wird ihr gut gehen, denn ich bleibe.

Bleibe bei ihr, für ewig aber seine.

Vorgänger

Manipulation (2016)

Zu viele Freundschaften entstehen heutzutage durch soziale Netzwerke. Sie sah Veto an den Treppen und es brauchte nur einen Klick, die seine Welt auf den Kopf gestellt hatte. Sie hat Ambitionen, wie auch andere, aber dieses Mal könnte man sagen, das Jahr wird viele aufregende Ereignisse haben. Man sollte wissen, was man tut, mit welcher Absicht. Mädchen wollen nur ihren Spaß. Auf welche emotionalen Kosten sie kommen, ist deren Sache.

Of Kith and Kin

A Moonraker's Tale

MAGS FLETCHER

Independently published in Great Britain by
She Wordsmiths

ISBN: 9798669316709

Cover design and other artwork by:
Steve Whitworth (Steve Whitworth Arts)

To the late Emma Chapman, ever present throughout my childhood and early adulthood. She inspired me to discover my roots and understand more about the generations who came before me.

'I finally wrote it, Nana'

FOREWORD

Mags Fletcher first put pen to paper, to write *Of Kith and Kin - A Moonraker's Tale* almost 30 years ago. Her novel lay unpublished. Today, in a world where anything is achievable, if you want it enough, it has become possible to bring the story - the characters and the places - back to life.

The author, herself from a family of Moonrakers (born of Middleton), has had an adult lifelong interest in genealogy. A desire to know her ancestry - to learn about the family who came before her. Many a day has been spent scouring records, searching overgrown graveyards, quizzing members for a snippet which would lead to another discovery.

It is those findings which brought the author to start to build a story. This story.

Of Kith and Kin is a historical fiction tale of late 19th century family life in working class Middleton. But to truly understand the roots of the book, and the passion that saw the author become so connected to her characters, it is worth first understanding a little history, of the town itself.

Middleton is situated around four miles north east of the city of Manchester. The Industrial Revolution brought first silk and then cotton to the town - although it was a centre for domestic cloth production (wool and flannel) even as far back as the middle ages. It is that path which leaves Middleton still very much remembered as a Lancashire mill town to this day.

JW Lees & Co Brewers also chose Middleton as its centre of brewing in the early part of the 19th century and remains ever present to this day. A fact which may explain the prominence of alehouses scattered throughout this book - about kith and kin in a Lancashire town.

Back to this novel, and life was very different then.

Families were larger, living was simpler, mortality rates and ages much younger. The strains placed on family life, we can only imagine, must have been incredible.

Times have moved on, of course. With progress comes a new view of what is permissible. Behaviour, language, use of terminology are now very much at the heart of anything we say or write. Things we would simply not consider correct or acceptable now were quite commonplace – or so we believe.

As a reader, it is worth remembering this tale is written to reflect a reality. One of family life, in a time when folk lived their lives quite differently. A hard, and sometimes wince-making reality. But a reality none the less.

And to help the reader immerse themselves entirely in that period, the author has intentionally chosen a more dated form of narrative English too. We are not talking Shakespeare here. But while modern editors, real or virtual, might well shy away from at the use of extended description, multiple adverbs and split infinitives, its use is there to demonstrate a time. And in speech, to hint at a perhaps a lesser education, class difference, or simply remind us of an affectionate Lancashire dialect which is still a part of who we are.

It is also important to say that the book, while inspired by the tales the author has listened to, as told by relatives and acquaintances over several decades, is a work of pure fiction. Any similarity to events and people, past or present is purely coincidental. It is a product of her imagination.

I do hope you enjoy taking a trip back down memory lane, as much as I did – and as Mags Fletcher clearly has too.

Marie T Smith
Writer of travel, photography and life reflections
as She Wordsmiths..

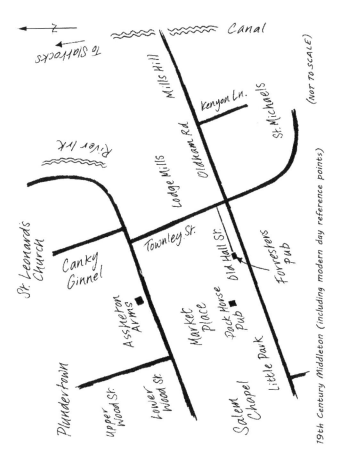

19th Century Middleton (including modern day reference points)

N

To Slattocks

Canal

Mills Hill

Kenyon Ln.

St. Michaels

River Irk

Lodge Mills

Oldham Rd.

St. Leonards Church

Townley St.

Canky Ginnel

Old Hall St.

Foresters Pub

Assheton Arms

Market Place

Pack Horse Pub

Plundertown

Upper Wood St.

Lower Wood St.

Salem Chapel

Little Park

(NOT TO SCALE)

iii

1914

MAGS FLETCHER

Prologue

A sudden whisper of wind rustled across the highest point of the burial ground, touching the sombre group of mourners in its passing. Its bitterness flicked with a vengeance at the skirts of the women, as with heads bowed and eyes misted, they saw only the coffin.

The graveyard was absolutely silent, but on this chilly overcast February day, the silence was all consuming, as their hearts and souls went out to Hannah.

Harry Shaw wasn't aware of the carefully delivered sermon or the sobbing and weeping of the women. He was pre-occupied, gazing into the distance in his own escape from the reality of the moment. With his back to St Leonard's church. He could just make out the hills of Oldham, sometimes easily visible, but today, shrouded in the familiar rolling grey mist.

A chill crept over him and shifting his feet on the wet miserable earth, his eyes wandered backed to the assembled gathering. Without concern, Harry realised they were watching him.

His sons, his daughters, their families – indeed all of them, were watching him. Their manner completely hostile, their intent – to cause him all his guilt.

Edith, his eldest daughter, very similar in looks and ways to that of her mother – was dabbing at her red-rimmed eyes, and between tears, glaring icily at her father. Jack, her husband was holding their young son in one arm and trying to afford Edith some comfort with the other.

Harry had insisted that all the grandchildren must be present; he felt he owed Hannah that much at least. She wouldn't have approved at all – wouldn't have approved of his way of doing things – could never have subjected the young ones to this. But he did.

The silent accusations flew at him from all angles as the grey-haired old man averted his own, very dry eyes from Edith's. Glancing momentarily at the youngsters who were becoming frozen, fractious, and somewhat bored, his eyes came to rest on Edward.

Standing true and proud as a Shaw ought to be, the carbon copy of the father bore his grief all too well. Harry thought he caught an encouraging smile from Edward, but he dismissed the very same thought as imagination.

Who the hell would be smiling at Harry Shaw?

Harry, the junior, stood facing his father; the strain of this solemn event deeply etched on his ashen face, as he struggled with dignity to contain the threatening tide of tears. Tears for Hannah, his mother in name only.

Movement and the shaking of hands brought Harry back to reality. It was over. The mourners, with one accord, began to filter away from the edge of the grave. Hesitant, almost reluctant to leave one of their ilk in such a solitary place.

Harry lingered until they were all gone from sight, then whispering quickly down towards the grave, lest he should be overheard, he said gently

''Tis over lass – for you, 'tis finished.'

He raised his head, glanced across the rooftops of Middleton, then added 'Listen, the town mourns for you Hannah. Can you hear? See how quiet it is now.'

For one last moment, they were together in silence.

'I'm sorry, lass. So sorry. I can't say enough.'

He felt a lone tear roll down his cheek. Hurriedly brushing it away, he thrust his hands deep into his pockets.

Unwilling, totally unsure as to what he should do next, Harry paused. Another moment – then he shuffled away down the incline towards Canky Ginnel. He would go back to the house alone – his own way – along through Market Place and on up Wood Street.

'Bugger 'em' he muttered to himself. They hadn't waited for him. Not one of them. Not even Edward.

There was no one to comfort Harry. No one to lend him an arm of support. Harry Shaw hadn't expected otherwise. He was a man alone; an island unto himself.

1874

1

'You sure you've said your prayers?' Hannah leaned over her youngest brother, tucking him into the bed he shared with Elizabeth, and affectionately tussling his fair hair.

'Yes,' James answered, dozily, his eyelids heavy with impending sleep 'love you, Hannah.'

'And I love you too.' She smiled broadly, bending to kiss his rosy cheeks. He was a good child, she mused, easy enough to care for.

Quietly. So as not to disturb him as he drifted off, Hannah went down the narrow stairs. She went out into the yard to collect the remaining washing before it became chilled by the cooler evening air.

Humming lightly to herself, she nodded neighbourly to the group of women, who were as usual tittle tattling at one end of the communal yard.

'If you'll be wanting your Alice,' from his open doorway, Tom spoke suddenly, catching Hannah unawares 'she's in here.'

'Oh, you gave me a turn then,' Hannah laughed, her arms full with dry washing 'you can send her home when you've had enough of her, Then she can fold this lot.'

It had been hard for Hannah without a mother. Esther, the eldest sister, managed to take over completely when Alice Adcock died while giving birth to young James. He coped magnificently but, nevertheless, Hannah had to share some of the burden. Aunt Sally took Alice and Elizabeth for a short while, giving the Adcocks some time to come to terms with their grief, but in the end. All responsibilities fell onto the girls' shoulders. Both Esther and Hannah looked to each other for support. That was until Esther, the elder, married and moved to Higher Wood Street. Then it was Hannah's turn to become the maternal figurehead.

The task didn't worry her too much. Life was life and there were families in worse situations.

7

Still only seventeen Hannah Adcock could bake, clean, wash, and run the household as well as any of the married women in the street. She took great pride in her own efficiency and was almost sure that some of her less fastidious neighbours harboured feelings of envy towards her. It worried her not as she cheerfully threw herself into making certain that her father's needs, and those of the children, were adequately provided for.

When not knee deep in domestic matters, Hannah found the church a great source of help and comfort. She would, without fail, winter and summer alike, have the family dressed in their Sunday best for services at St Michael's in Tonge. Alice Adcock was buried there, and Hannah felt as if she were showing her mother the growing family, each time they attended service. It pleased her to feel that her mother, although not with them in body, was close at hand.

Folding the dried bed sheets, having decided not to leave them for Alice, she realized the front door was still wide open. The evening air was cooling, and she could feel a draught around her ankles. Leaving her chore, she went to close the door.

Popping her head outside, she glanced up and down the street, to see Beth playing ring taw with her friends. It was something Hannah had missed out on; her childhood disappearing in an instant the day her mother died.

'Don't go away,' Hannah shouted as she caught Beth's eye 'you are coming in soon.'

'I won't,' Beth answered, still absorbed in the game.

Hannah, half turning to go indoors, sensed someone at Tom and Ada's front. Something instinctively caused her to glance in that direction.

Their eyes met.

Raising his cap, he mumbled 'howdo?' then smiled broadly.

Hannah felt a sudden rush of blood to her cheeks. She knew she was blushing profusely.

'Oh hello,' she managed to return the greeting. Though her own self confidence was ebbing by the second, as his eyes held her gaze. His face twinkled warmly, the while, his wide smile breaking down her defences. Time seemed to stand still. She began to feel uncomfortable and embarrassed under his close scrutiny, aware of her heart thumping rapidly in her chest. She wondered if he could sense his effect on her. She realized he must surely.

Relief flooded through her as Tom appeared at the doorway. Hannah, thankful for the interruption, turned and beat a hasty retreat.

Closing her own front door, though a little too quickly, Hannah leaned heavily against it, confused by her thoughts and feelings.

'Oh my,' she said aloud, one hand across her heaving breast 'and so bold.' The experience had unnerved her more than she cared to admit. She'd had admirers before, but this one was completely different.

This one was Harold Shaw.

She knew all about Harold Shaw. In fact, everyone knew all about Harold Shaw.

Hannah shivered involuntarily as all the tales and gossip about him began to flit through her head. Abundant tales and gossip which confirmed his lack of good character. Nevertheless, she understood instantly what it was that made him so attractive.

He was a fine figure of a man. A man with the most beautiful blue eyes she had ever seen. Capable of reducing her to a quivering wreck. The clean-cut moustache on his upper lip seemed to make his warm smile all the more appealing.

Hannah took a deep breath, suddenly feeling foolish, as she mentally appraised the man's charming good features.

'I'm back!' Alice's voice, loud and musical, ringing from the back of the house, brought Hannah back to the immediate reality. 'That Harry is in there, so I have come home.'

'Um,' Hannah responded, seeming unaffected 'I saw him go in.'

'Good looking,' Alice commented, rolling her eyes in a saucy fashion.

'I hadn't really noticed,' Hannah answered quickly, her fingers crossed tightly behind her back, her voice attempting to show her indifference.

2

Didn't expect to see you here.' Tom said, inviting Harry through the house to sit on the back step with him 'expect to see you at the pit; not here.'

'I wanted to take another look at yon lass,' Harry grinned roguishly 'though I never thought I'd walk into her.'

'I might have known it,' the older man shook his head, negatively 'she's not for you lad.'

'Aye, but I'll maybe change that,' Harry said decisively.

'Huh, 'tis you that'll have to change.'

'Maybe. But not too much. She flushed to the roots when she saw me.'

'Aye. Only because she's not had any dealings with the likes of you,' Tom winked, nudging Harry in the ribs with his elbow 'you'll have embarrassed the lass.'

'Nay. I'd say she liked what she saw.' Harry laughed, Arrogant and self-assured.

'Well I'll tell you now, I wouldn't dally with her,' Tom advised seriously 'and that's a bit of talk worth heeding.'

'Aw c'mon Tom,' Harry grinned, ignoring is work mate's serious tone 'I'll wager she'll be Mrs. Shaw before too long.'

'Now you're talking soft lad.' Tom was beginning to sound angry at the thoughts of a man with Harry's reputation so set on dallying with a decent god-fearing lass.

'Nay Tom.'

'She's a church goer Harry; and right decent she is. Not for you at all,' Tom tried to make the lad see sense. 'She's from gradely folks and it wouldn't be proper for you to muck about with her.'

'She'll see me at church come Sunday. I'll show her I'm not mucking about,' Harry said adamantly, inwardly amused by Tom's manner.

'Aye and you'll have 'em all gawping'

'I'll be noticed, then, won't I?'

'Harold Shaw in St Michael's will be the talk of Middleton. Not just for a day, but for weeks to come.' Tom took a sidelong glance at Harry. 'You'll have to live up to it.'

'I'll do it.'

'Why all this Harry when you usually do as you please? I can't for the life of me see what you're up to. Why?'

'Maybe it's about time I started thinking of settling down,' Harry said, this time seriously. 'You know? Getting me a family and a place of my own.'

'Oh nay, Harry,' Tom bellowed with laughter, 'that's not you. Not in keeping with your character at all. You had a knock on the head?'

'You'll see!' Harry glared, vexed suddenly 'You'll see in time.'

'Oh, don't take on so,' Tom sighed, realizing he had now raised Harry's temper. 'Calm down lad. Just have a good think on it. Because you'll need to. And you'll need to mend your ways.'

Harry rose from the step, trust his hands into his pockets. Tom watched as he paced the yard like a caged animal.

It seemed like an age but could only have been moments when Harry spoke. His anger now subsided he calmly said 'I've made up my mind Tom.'

'I've seen Hannah Adcock, and I want her.'

And so, with a deviousness that was second nature to Harry, he planned his courtship of the barely attainable Hannah Adcock down to the finest detail. He knew without any doubt that it was her father who would need to be swayed into accepting him. Hannah, he assumed, wouldn't prove too difficult. If he played the game slowly, sensitively, she would succumb. Frank Adcock was the only obstacle.

Harry though long and hard on his course of action. Pleasing the father wasn't the usual way. Having answered to no man in the past, it rankled him somewhat. But to achieve his sole aim, Harry knew he must curb his own lifestyle. He would have to become a decent upstanding figure of the community. The thought creased him. It would be hard but by God, he would do it. Nothing would stop him.

By his own sheer determination and willpower, Harry was indeed present at St Michael's service the following Sunday – and for every Sunday afterwards.

He paid no attention to the sermons. He only weakly managed to mouth the words to hymns he had never heard before. All the while watching Hannah continually. She relieved the boredom for him, brightened the tedium. Each week, positioning himself such that the Adcocks couldn't fail to notice his attendance. Harry would take great pains to catch her eye. Hannah would bow her head hastily, a flush on her cheeks. Yet appearing to all and sundry to be deep in prayer. Harry knew prayer was not the cause, and it pleased him to see the reaction his glances produced.

As the services came to an end Harry would quickly vacate his pew, dash smartly outside the church and make himself available to pass the time of day with other churchgoers. He needed to impress and to be seen as acceptable, as the Adcocks emerged.

But Frank Adcock was not taken in for a moment. He would be completely offhand whenever Harry made an approach in their direction. Terse when the lad spoke. Hannah would blush and turn away, embarrassed. Alice would cover her mouth with a gloved hand, stifling girlish giggles at so bold an admirer.

But Harry was undeterred. He kept up the same routine. Week in. Week out.

He would win.

4

Harry began to realise that, to see even more of Hannah, all he needed to do was to visit his workmate, Tom, more often. It was so simple he could have kicked himself. Why had he not cottoned on sooner?

Hannah was a regular neighbour, dropping in on Tom and Ada several times a day. It thrilled Harry to the core. To be so close to the object of his desire, without her father being in constant attendance, gave Harry the chance to get to know her with ease. And for Hannah to start to accept his presence.

Conversation with her was guarded for a time. But she warmed to him and found it easier to speak when Tom and Ada joined the general banter.

At first, when Hannah realised what Harry was up to, she found it disconcerting and could have easily dashed back home. But his just being there, held her. She was fascinated by the man, totally in awe of his self-assurance. Gradually she began to unfold in Harry's company until the day dawned when she would begin to hope to find him at Ada's house. She felt silly to keep popping next door on some pretext. Just to see if he was there - in case she may have missed his arrival. But good sense had, all but, disappeared.

Hannah had fallen, quite easily, for the charming Harry Shaw.

It was Ada who brough matters to a head one evening. Harry had been a constant visitor for more than a month. She'd also know why Hannah, full of the jitters, couldn't stay home these days either.

'You pair should be doing your courting elsewhere' Tom's wife said 'then I can have some peace in my own home. She was quite unaffected by the reactions her words might cause.

Hannah turned crimson. Averting her gaze from Harry, she grinned.

'We're not courting' said Harry, amused by Ada's words but to save Hannah further embarrassment.

'Ah well then lad' Ada clucked knowingly 'I've seen the likes of courting before and I know how it starts. I can see the signs, plain as the nose on my face. If ever a pair were smitten bad, then it's the both of you. You're in here, night and day, grinning and blushing, coming over all affected. I'm not daft, you know. I wasn't born yesterday either. I have seen it all before.'

'Give over Ada' Tom butted in, carefully tapping out his pipe n the hearth 'you're embarrassing the pair. 'Tis not your business.'

'I'd best be making tracks.' Harry rose from his chair, hoping to spare Hannah any further suffering. He knew this was causing her deep concern and assumed his exit would be easier for her.

'You'll see Hannah to her door before you go traipsing off,' Ada grinned, arms folded across her chest, her manner decisive 'and while you're about it, ask her father can you call upon her. And put a stop to this nonsense.'

Inwardly, Harry bubbled excitedly. This was his chance! The chance he had been waiting for. And it was Ada who had engineered it. He could hardly contain himself.

'Go on,' Ada smiled, pleased with the way she'd handled things 'be off with you.'

o0o

There was no light showing inside when Harry and Hannah stood, self-consciously, outside the front door. He shuffled, agitated, as she huddled against the wall, nervously.

'You should have gone in the back way,' Harry whispered, concerned in case any sound brought Frank Adcock to investigate. And so, terminate their few snatched moments together.

'Nay,' Hannah answered, twisting her shawl into a tight knot 'father will be in the back.'

'Ah,' he muttered, slowly moving closer, but not too close as to scare her 'you're not cold?'

'Nay,' she mumbled, her eyes cast downwards, seeing only the toes of her clogs.

'Hannah,' he moved closer, his insides churning wildly. He wanted to catch hold of her and crush her body against his. But instinct told him to hold back, even though he could feel the growing tension between them. His nerves were taut, his breath now shallow as he gazed longingly at her.

'Aye,' she raised her eyes and caught a twinkle from his. It warmed her through and through. Glowing with anticipation she felt her heart begin to race. She was sure he would hear it beating within her breast. In the still of the night, he was so handsome. And his good humour making her forget the tales about him, bandied about. Suddenly she no longer cared for other folks' gossip.

'C-c - can I - can I hold you. Just for a moment?' he asked. Throwing caution to the wind, he was sure the time was right. He was sure she was ready to respond to his embrace.

Hannah visibly stiffened, dropping the knotted edge of her shawl. Nervously she answered 'aye. But mind 'tis only a minute.'

He caught her to him instantly, folding his arms around her. Gentle yet possessive. Tightly locked against him, she felt his warmth; his strength; and it pleased her in a way she never imagined.

Harry felt her trembling, in the comfort of his arms, and hugged her tighter, in an effort to calm her. Her sweet, clean smell drifted into his nostrils as he nestled against her hair. It was a good feeling. Hannah in his arms, The night, silent and unmoving, all around them. He felt drunk. Intoxicated by her nearness. He wanted to shout out his gut feelings from the rooftops. But he didn't. Harry kept himself under control, tethering his wild spirit.

Suddenly, he felt Hannah begin to pull away. Harry, with some disappointment, immediately relinquished his hold on her saying 'shall I come and ask your father now, or will the morrow be best?'

'Best wait,' Hannah cautioned, now at odds with herself, 'I'll have words with him first. He doesn't think too kindly of you.'

'Ah, I know,' Harry agreed, understanding the problem his approach to Frank Adcock might cause. He knew the man didn't like Harry at all.

'You'd best get yourself indoors or you'll be taking a chill. I'll make tracks. It wouldn't do if he saw me standing on the doorstep without his knowing.'

Bending hastily, catching Hannah totally unawares, Harry brushed his lips quickly across her cheek.

'Oh!' she gasped. Startled, she stepped bac, her hand rising to cover the place his lips had touched.

'See you in Tom's tomorrow' Harry grinned cheekily, turning to sprint down 'and mind you sleep tight lass.'

Hannah watched in awe and astonishment, as Harry disappeared from view. Then and only then did she dare to knock on her front door.

'I've got a mind to wed,' Harry announced casually. They all stopped eating, staring open-mouthed in amazement.

It was his mother, who, having rapidly recovered from the initial shock, asked 'what's brought this on of a sudden?'

'Eh,' Harry scratched his head, as his brothers looked on, grinning in amusement.

'Gone soft he has' Albert erupted, filling the kitchen with his coarse laughter.

'Shut up lad,' Jane chided 'let's hear what Harry has to say for himself'.

Leaning back on his chair, Harry smiled. The family was sniggering now, almost choking on their tea. Not that he cared. His mind was made up. Nothing, not even their derision, would stop him now. He couldn't tell what was going through his mother's head. She wasn't smiling. Jane Shaw appeared puzzled. She would, in her own quiet way, weigh it all up before speaking her mind.

'Is the lass with child?' Jane asked. Her manner serious, her brow heavily furrowed with lines of worry.

'Nay, mother – nay,' Harry relaxed, clasped his hands together behind his head.

'If it's that Hannah you've been sweet on,' Bill guffawed, 'I'll wager she'll stay untouched no matter who she weds.'

'Watch your mouth Bill' Harry barked, angry that his elder brother should talk of Hannah in such a coarse fashion.

'Aye,' Jane agreed 'there's no need of talk like that at my table, lad.'

'Aw, mother,' Bill attempted to defend himself 'she is a bit uppity. Not of our kind. Too fancy by half.'

'What's wrong with that?' Harry demanded, leaning forward in his chair 'A bit of class, that's what she's got. You'd do well to find a lass like her.'

'Nay, Harry,' Bill grinned, 'I'll stick to my own kind.'

'Aye,' Albert offered, 'you're more at home with the rough and ready.'

They both roared with laughter, enjoying the thoughts of pleasures to be had from the less moral lasses they associated with.

'Umm,' Jane pondered, ignoring her son's coarse references, 'has she an idea of what you're up to?'

'Nay,' Harry grinned oafishly, 'not yet.'

'You've not asked her then?' Bill asked, wide eyed astonished.

'Nay,' Harry answered.

'You should be asking her,' Jane proffered. 'before your fancy ideas go too far. It's as your brothers say, she's not in the same class as us – and besides which, there's that father of hers. Pretty strict he is and by all accounts, not one to let any of his daughters go off with good for nothings like you.'

'I work hard enough,' Harry defended himself 'and always have done.'

'Aye and you play hard enough too,' Jane cackled knowingly, 'and you'll have to start putting your brass away, instead of wasting it on ale.'

'I won't change my mind.' Harry remained adamant.

'Like your father, aren't you?' Jane smiled affectionately. Her face softening. 'Once you've got a mind to anything it has to be done. Aye, many a time I've had with him and his ways. You're no different.'

'It's alright with you then?' Harry asked.

''Tis up to you lad, don't ask me. Ask her,' Jane sighed 'but I can't see it coming off. And if it did, well, it won't be a good mix. But I'll tell you this and I'll tell it straight. If it don't mix, you'll have made your bed, lad, and you'll lie on it.' She pointed at him repeatedly 'and there'll be no place here for you and your troubles once you've done it. Because I know you, Harry. I've raised you and I know how bad you can be.'

Harry stared at her, unbelieving. His mother was a strong woman. Although now grey and withered, old before her time, she was full of strong will. A coarse woman, she had needed to be hard when bringing up such wayward sons through these years, without a father's hand. Compassion, sympathy, heart – call it what you will – had no place in Jane Shaw's life.

'There's no need to look at me like that, either,' she said coldly, 'I've put up with your ways for long enough. If you wed the lass, she'll have it to reckon with. God help her is all I can say.

'So, you see Harry, once you go, it'll be for good.'

'Mother!' he exclaimed, 'I only said I had a mind to wed.'

'Aye I know,' she grinned wickedly, 'and damned fine chance it is of getting at least one of you off my tired old hands.'

'Mother. I'm your son and you are throwing me out.'

'Nay lad, I've enough on my plate with these half-wits,' motioning to his brothers. Then tapping the side of her head, she added 'they've nowt up here, 'tis all in the britches. Leastways you do have a few wits. About the only normal one among us all. Just look at Sally here with her crossed eyes and Lizzie with her withered leg. Go on lad, go, and wed your fancy lass, if she'll have you. Just don't come back here. We don't want her do-gooding ways, which by all accounts is all she's full of.'

'She's a gradely lass, mother,' Harry accentuated.

'Too good for you.'

'I say good on him,' young Herbert spoke for the first time. Being slow it had taken him long to digest the conversations around him.

'Thanks, Herby,' Harry grinned, patting him on the shoulder affectionately.

'She's gradely,' Herby repeated, pleased he had his brother's approval.

'Shut up lad, you don't know what we're talking about,'

21

Jane said.

'I do,' he grinned, saliva oozing from the corners of his loosely held lips, 'I do.'

They all laughed in one accord, understanding that although half-witted as he was, Herbert was quite certain as to what they had been discussing.

'C'mon,' Jane said harshly, 'get your faces fed and let's hear no more of this nonsense for the time being. There'll be time enough for talk if Harry does wed the lass.'

6

'Alice, Elizabeth,' Frank Adcock peered at the two girls, sat reading at the table 'time you were up the stairs.'

Hannah looked up from the sewing in her lap and caught her father's eye.

'I want a word with you,' he said to her. Then back to the two girls, 'c'mon you won't be keeping your good looks if you're out of them beds too long.'

'Try not to waken James,' Hannah added.

'He always wakens' Alice said.

'Aye,' Frank muttered. 'The noise from the pair of you would wake the dead.'

The girls looked at each other, then with heads bowed, giggled, hoping the father wouldn't hear. Gathering their books together and scraping back their chairs, they bid him and Hannah goodnight, then as silently as possible, went upstairs.

'I'm going to listen,' Alice whispered to Beth as they reached the top of the stairs 'go and make sure James is fast asleep because if I am caught, we'll both be in deep trouble.'

'I don't think you should,' Beth said worriedly, 'it'll be a private matter.'

'Go on,' Alice pressed 'I'll creep back down and then come back and tell you what's said.'

'Oh, Alice you'll get in real bother if father catches you.'

'Don't be soft. I won't get caught. Now go on.' Then treading lightly, with the stealth borne of years of practice, Alice negotiated the stairs, carefully bypassing the creaky steps, until she was far enough down to hear with ease.

'That Harry wants to wed you,' Frank looked his daughter directly in the eye.

'Ah, I see' Hannah said, non-committal.

'Is that all you can say?' he asked, puzzled.

'What can I say, father,' Hannah sighed. Harry Shaw had persistently made himself known to her. At one point it had seemed as if the man was lurking around every corner. Determined in his effort to meet with her at every possible opportunity. There were no other suitors. Harry had seen to that.

'I don't want him for a son-in-law,' Frank spoke thoughtfully. 'He's not good enough for any lass of mine.'

'He's not as bad as he's made out to be,' Hannah said defensively.

'You don't know that, lass.'

'We've become quite good friends, father, I do see a lot of him' she continued.

'Aye, too much as is good for you.'

'He's a hard worker,' Hannah felt herself flush, 'I think he's really keen.'

'Been spooning have you?' Frank asked suddenly.

Hannah didn't answer. Squirming uncomfortably in her chair, her face turned red. She couldn't help but remember the feel of his lips on hers. The warm comfortable feelings which swept over her when he held her tight. She was pleased, yet a little afraid. Afraid of the way Harry Shaw affected her.

'Ah lass, I can see you have.' Frank was vexed. 'But I don't like it. I don't want a decent daughter of mine, behaving like this kind of woman. You're a good lass, I know it.'

Hannah watched her father carefully out of the corner of her eye. She saw clenched fists resting on the arms of the chair and noted the tight set of his mouth. He was thinking about Harry, she knew, weighing up in his mind what to do.

He spoke again, presently, his voice without emotion. 'I don't like him, lass, he's not for you. I know he's tried. Tried to be more respectable, but he's the sort that'll never change. Oh, I can see he's been trying to win me over. And he's been putting ideas in your head by the looks of it. We can do without him.'

'I don't know what to say,' Hannah responded quietly,

her heart sinking with every word her father uttered.

'He keeps on asking me. All the time going on and on at me,' Frank sighed. 'If it was anyone else...'

'What is so wrong with him?' she asked with caution.

Frank simply stared at her; his lips set tight. He could see it in her face. She was besotted with Harry Shaw. Of all the decent men available, men who would be only too glad to wed Hannah, she had to forego them. For what? Admittedly, Harry has been attending church service regularly and keeping away from his more usual haunts. But Frank didn't believe in old dogs and new tricks, even if Harry did seem lily white of late.

'What about Billy Green, or that Samuel what's his name. Wouldn't they be better prospects?'

'Nay, father, please don't wish any of them on me,' aghast she replied. 'I love Harry.'

'I knew it,' Frank jumped out of his seat and stood squarely in front of her. 'What's he done to you?' he demanded.

'Nothing!' she answered honestly. 'I'm ashamed you should think so little of him – and of me.'

He turned his back to her. Leaning on the mantelpiece he stared into the fire. His mind working furiously to find a solution. He hated Harry. Hated everything the man stood for. Yet at the same time, he didn't want to cause any disconnect between himself and Hannah. She'd been a good lass. In fact, she was everything a father could wish for. To him, she was worth more than her weight in gold. He wanted her happiness above all else. But he was wary of Harry and this feeling made him want to protect her from the very object of her love.

'I could send you along when James goes off to stay with our Ben. It would only be for a while until all this nonsense has passed.'

'It wouldn't change anything.' Hannah visibly paled at the thought, her insides in turmoil.

'A little time away from him,' he suggested.

'Please don't, father, you need me here,' she implored.

'I dare say we could manage for a short while,' he smiled encouragingly. He rubbed his chin thoughtfully and added 'I'll have words with Esther and Abe and see what they think.'

Hannah felt tears spring to her eyes. She bent her head quickly lest her father should see. This was all so unfair. She'd been competent enough to keep house for years, yet now she was unable to have any say in her own future. It was to be decided for her and she hurt, deeply.

oOo

'You won't be marrying Harry then?' Alice whispered in the quiet of the bedroom, sure that Hannah was weeping in the darkness.

'You've been listening!' Hannah accused fiercely.

'Aye and I'm glad' Alice smile to herself smugly.

'You should have your nose cut off' Hannah turned angrily in her bed to face her sister. 'It has nothing to do with you, so mind your own business.'

'*But I love him*' Alice mimicked, sniggering into her pillow.

'You're like a child,' Hannah said, refusing to be drawn by her sister's antics.

'Ha! And you're a woman. And we all know why!' sarcastically Alice taunted her.

'Mind your tongue, Alice, and go to sleep. I have no need for your silliness.' Hannah turned her back.

'Well he's no good,' Alice persisted, determined to have her say, 'and I have heard he's got many a lass into trouble.'

'How dare you say things like that.' Hannah rolled back and sharply smacked Alice across the mouth as her anger finally erupted. 'You should get that mouth of yours scrubbed out, lady.'

''Tis true. You'll see.' Alice turned her back on

Hannah, hand covering her smarting face, but content she had said her piece.

'I'd say you were jealous Alice Adcock, Right jealous at that.'

No answer came from her sister. Hannah lay silently, the tears pricking her eyes as she thought of Harry and the things that had been said, this night. She began to pray, and pray hard, as she hoped that all would come right in the end.

Her belief was that it would.

oOo

Hannah made the excuse that she needed to walk to clear her head. It was true. Her head was pounding savagely, but she knew no walk would ease it. She needed to have some time alone, time to think things over. Her father hadn't broached the subject in a week now and she was desperately unhappy. Living each day in a thoroughly miserable state.

Aimlessly she wandered towards Mills Hill. She noticed no-one. Totally oblivious to all and sundry she found the seclusion she sought alongside the canal bank.

She sighed as she found a pleasing stretch of grass to sit on. Idly picking around her, on the ground, she picked and lazily tossed small pebbles into the quiet waters of the canal. It was as she watched the poetic rippling on the surface, Harry came upon her.

'I didn't know if I'd find you,' he smiled warmly. He was breathless having rushed to catch up with her.

'I knew you would.' She turned to look up at him, her face showing her troubled thoughts, 'did Tom tell you where I'd be?'

'Aye, he did.' Harry flopped down beside her and caught her hand as she flicked it upwards to toss another stone into the canal. 'What ails you?'

'It's father.' She turned and looked directly into his

eyes. He saw the sadness. 'He isn't going to let us wed.'

Harry sighed. He threw his arm around her shoulders and hugged her hard. Ideas were churning through his mind.

They sat for a while, content to be as they were for the moment. Neither speaking. Together but alone with their thoughts.

Presently, Harry spoke, his voice gentle and warm 'No need to worry, lass, we'll wed alright.'

''Tis impossible Harry.' She glanced at him soulfully.

'We will!'. Harry was adamant. 'I will ask him again. And I'll keep right on asking until he gets sick of the sight of me.'

Reaching out to her, he brushed the dampness from her cheeks. Dampness where tears had fallen, and he realised at that moment he felt a consuming love for her. Until now desire and lust had driven him on, but never the need and want he was experiencing now. He felt protective and strong for them both.

As she leaned her head against his chest, Harry folded both his arms around her. Finding no resistance, he pulled her gently down onto the grass. He wanted her now, wanted her more than anything else imaginable. They both took pleasure from the heady nearness of each other's warmth. Whispering his love for her, softly, soothing, Harry felt her yield and mould herself to him. He smothered her face, her hair, her neck in the kisses he knew would ease her troubles.

Slowly Hannah began to respond to his expertise. A heady mix of delirium and abandonment. Her sighing arousing Harry's ardour to a pitch he found difficult to control. As the evening shadows gathered, hiding them from prying eyes, Harry in his blind passion took hold of her hand. Breathlessly bold he pushed it down between them, holding her firmly in place against his throbbing rigidity. Groaning with pleasure he moved his hips, grinding with fervour against her palm.

It was a moment before Hannah realised what he was doing and what their actions were leading to. A hot flood of shock and shame rushed through her. Quickly pulling her hand from his grasp as if the very act had seared her flesh she jumped to her feet.

'Oh no!' Covering her face with both hands in embarrassment Hannah felt the tears prick her eyes.

Harry was on his feet and beside her in an instant. With soothing words of comfort and concern, he said ''Tis alright, Hannah, I wasn't going to hurt you.'

'Oh my God, what have we done?' she wailed, her face still registering shock. 'It's wrong Harry, so wrong. I am ashamed.'

Moving closer and pulling her gently to him, he murmured 'Nay Hannah, you've no cause for shame. We've done no wrong. 'Tis not for a man to say but...' he hesitated, trying to read her mood, then stumbled on 'I love you lass. There's no wrong in loving.'

Warily she held herself away from him. Afraid of him. Afraid of her own emotions. She was thoroughly ashamed of what could have happened had better sense not prevailed. The tears began to flow as all Harry's attempts to console her, failed.

'C'mon lass we'd better make tracks,' he said eventually, leading her onto the track by the canal.

Silently she allowed him to steer her homewards, linking his arm, but keeping enough distance between them. Hannah was horrified at the slightest contact with his body, scared he might become inflamed with desire again. She could not cope with it, could not understand how she had almost succumbed to his advances.

Harry accepted the silence, sensing the tension within her. Desperately holding his fervour in check, he took sidelong glances at her. He knew he would have to tread softly in his attempt to keep her.

He'd not had a woman in ages and this self-imposed celibacy was causing him anguish. But he couldn't rush her too much. The sooner he wed her the better it would be.

His thoughts began to wander as he mentally toyed with the idea of appeasing his hunger elsewhere. Hannah was not ready yet. And he was sure she would never know if he found his pleasures in other directions. At least it would spare her the torment, and such guilt, of having to fend off his amorous advances.

His mind made up he quickened his pace. Anxious to get Hannah home suddenly and leave him with enough time to find a willing lass at the alehouse.

Harry with unusual caution rapped on the partly open front door.

There were children out playing in the street and a huddled group of miner's wives idly chatting on the corner as he approached. Ada, Tom's wife was on her hands and knees, fiercely scrubbing her own front step as Harry walked by. Recognising he footfall she looked up, commenting on the sudden flush of good weather, her cautious eye trying to determine the purpose of Harry's visit to the Adcock's.

Ada already had an idea. She had expected it for some time, but nevertheless felt a pang of sorrow for the lad. There was nought she could do to help him, Nought she could say. Harry was so strong minded, and pig headed. He'd have to sort out his own troubles.

'Come in,' they both heard Frank's answer to his knocking.

Warily Harry pushed the door open wide and stepped in, shouting as he did, 'shall I close it behind me?'

'Aye lad, you'd best do,' came the answer.

Harry closed it, thankful that Ada wouldn't overhear what was said inside.

'You'd better sit yourself down, lad.' Frank spoke brusquely, without so much as glancing at Harry. 'I had a thought you'd be coming around.'

Harry removed his cloth cap and sat himself opposite Frank, looking around him in anticipation.

'You've no need to look for Hannah,' Frank noticed his watchful eye 'she's off visiting with her sisters.'

'Ah,' Harry mumbled quietly, his spirits sinking somewhat.

'So, why've you come?'

Harry, slowly turning his cap between his fingers, deliberately not looking at the older man, said 'I've come about getting wed.'

Frank sighed. Then shifting his position, growled 'you've had my answer lad, and I'll hear no more.'

'We both want to,' Harry insisted, his eyes cold with fierce determination, 'and we'll wait if we have to. But I want Hannah and I've no doubts she wants me.'

Frank snarled, his lips curling. 'So that's the way of it then?'

'Aye it is Mr. Adcock' Harry answered, then rushing on 'and all of it, it's making Hannah unhappy as well.'

'Don't you think I know that?' Frank shouted, the veins now standing out in his temples. 'She is of my blood and I can see what ails her. You've caused it – caused the lot of it. You just couldn't keep away from her. Couldn't leave her alone.'

'She can't stay with you forever,' Harry said boldly.

'Nay, but she could have found better than you,' Frank rose and stood directly in front of Harry. 'She's a good lass and I don't want you messing her about. I don't even like you, don't like you at all. Can't stand the sight of you. Granted you've tried to be more respectable, but your reputation isn't up to much is it?'

'I've changed, Mr. Adcock, sir. I've mended my ways a lot.' Harry now grovelling, he kept a tight hold of his own rising anger. He was determined to win and knew he must stay calm at all costs. Anyone else talking to him in this way would have been thumped black and blue by now. But this moment called for complete control.

'By all appearances you have, but its what's underneath that troubles me, lad.' Frank sat down again, his anger subsiding.

'I can't do any more than I have, sir,' Harry's voice was still calm. Then adding in his own defence 'maybe if I'd had a father, I wouldn't have been so wild.'

'Aye, there's something to be said about that.'

'It's been hard for my mother, bringing us up without a man around,' Harry continued, certain he was beginning to see the older man softening, 'her ways are not the best, but she wasn't to know.'

'Aye, lad, aye,' Frank muttered thoughtfully, understanding the way it must have been for a woman on her own.

'And I have always worked - and worked hard.'

'That's in your favour.' Frank allowed a smile to break through, all the time watching the other's face for an outward sign of the inner man.

'Thank you, sir.' Harry smiled, knowing now that Frank was thawing a little.

'I'll tell you what,' Frank had an idea. 'I was thinking of sending Hannah away for a time, but I know in my heart she doesn't want that. I won't give you an answer yet. Wait awhile. Maybe another year or so. And then we'll see. By then, maybe you might both have seen sense and gone your separate ways.'

Harry fixed a delighted smile on his face to show his gratitude.

Inwardly he groaned.

'Will that suit you?' Frank asked, pleased with himself.

'Aye.' Harry rose, leaning forward to shake his hand. He wasn't satisfied at all; he was unhappy about the whole thing. But Frank Adcock was calling the tune and he'd have to dance to it until such time as Frank was ready to stop playing.

'Be off home now lad,' Frank barked 'and I'll tell Hannah, you can come around later. You'll be wanting to talk I expect.'

'Thank you, Mr. Adcock, sir.' Harry backed out of the room, his heart heavy, anger still bubbling inside him. He wasn't used to not getting his way.

Ada was standing by her front door as Harry stepped outside.

She saw him smash his balled fist against the wall in temper. She clucked disapprovingly as he turned and snarled in her direction.

'You've made a right mess of that hand, Harry, lad' she

33

commented as he passed, noticing the blooded scrapes on his knuckles.

'Bugger off!' he growled, thrusting the injured hand in his pocket.

'Bad-tempered cuss,' she spat back, then stepped inside quickly, lest he should by chance decide to vent his anger on her.

8

Hannah lay still. Almost rigid, afraid to move, afraid of breathing. Afraid in case anything should stir Harry, who was, for the moment, slumbering contentedly, his arm slung possessively across her breast.

She couldn't hear any sounds from the other bedroom and prayed fervently none had heard. The embarrassment at such a thought causing her cheeks to flame in the darkness surrounding her.

It hadn't been as she expected it to be. They'd told her what to anticipate. Ada – well married with an abundance of advice. Esther – with equal words of knowledge and a jar of soothing salve, necessary she had said to ease soreness and pain.

But it hadn't been like that!

Hannah could still feel the sticky wetness between her legs and knew instinctively that it wasn't the gushing blood they had said it would be. There was no pain, no soreness, just an overwhelming feeling of shame, lest her father or sisters had overheard.

Hannah had laid rigid. They'd told her that was what she must do. She had clenched her teeth until her jaw ached and waited with eyes tightly closed for Harry to take his pleasure of the body that now belonged to him.

But it wasn't that way at all.

Her mind raced, completely wide awake, going back over the day's events and her mounting panic as the wedding festivities came all too quickly to an end. Trying to remember every detail. Piecing everything together, Hannah found her thoughts kept coming back to the moment when they were finally alone. Man and wife.

Harry had slid into bed alongside her. Not as a demented maniac but gentle and with warmth. He had held her close for what seemed like an age, all the while tenderly and gently wakening her. With soft kisses, he whispered words of love and encouragement. Presently her body relaxed, her eyes opened in amazement at the feelings he could rest from her. Her mouth gave itself readily to his expertise.

Slowly, with knowledge gained from years of making love to women, Harry coaxed her. He wrung every pleasurable feeling from her virgin body until both their passions became so intense, he slid, with ease, into her velvet softness. A softness that beckoned him.

There was no pain for Hannah. The moment they became as one, she felt a wonderful warmth spread outwards from between her legs, reaching to the very tips of her fingers. He thrust into causing moans of ecstasy to escape from her lips in sheer abandonment. And then with a groan and one final strong thrust, his movements ceased.

Slowly regaining her senses, and marvelling at how wonderful she felt, Hannah realised she was clasping him to her with great fervour. Her legs, immodestly, as wide apart as possible. She felt a warmth, a closeness she couldn't describe. An intense love for Harry. She couldn't understand why she had enjoyed the experience at all when all the advice had been to the contrary.

Harry kissed her gently, and with care slid away from her, leaving one arm across her. Within minutes she knew he was already asleep. She felt content.

o0o

'Ere' Hannah handed a small jar to her sister, 'you may as well have it back now.'

'Keep it' Esther shook her head, 'I can get some more. Besides, it comes in handy.'

'I don't need it.'

'What!' Esther exclaimed, rising from her knees, leaving the black-leading for the moment 'all newlyweds need extra help.'

Hannah blushed profusely as Esther peered into the jar. 'You've not used any?'

'I didn't need it' Hannah said quietly.

'You mean you haven't done it?' Esther blurted out.

'Oh aye, of course we have, Hannah answered quickly.

'In that case, you must have needed it,' Esther spoke with a firm knowledge of such matters, everyone does, especially the first time.'

Hannah didn't speak. She lowered her eyes, avoiding her sister's direct gaze.

'Oh my,' Esther cried, shocked, 'you – oh Hannah – it wasn't the first time?'

'Course it was, what do you think I am?' Hannah returned defensively.

'It can't have been if you didn't need this,' Esther waved the jar under Hannah's nose, brandishing it as if it was irrefutable evidence.

'Well, I didn't need it. And it was the first time. So, you are quite wrong.' Hannah said, adamant.

'I don't understand. Aren't you the least bit sore?'

'No.'

'Didn't it hurt?'

'No,' Hannah answered honestly 'you said it would and I expected it to. But it didn't. Isn't wasn't like you said.'

'Oh, Hannah.' Esther said, a sympathetic look on her face.

'*Oh Hannah*' what?' Hannah asked, puzzled.

'You're quite sure you've done it proper?' then Esther added quickly 'because if not then you're not married proper.'

'Don't be silly Esther, Harry knows all about such things.' Hannah began to blush.

'Are you sure?' Esther questioned, searchingly.

'Of course, I am sure,' Hannah said adamantly, vexed her intelligence should be questioned 'we've done it six times, so we've obviously done something!'

'Oh-my-Hannah' Esther's hand flew to her breast 'he's a beast.'

'What are you talking about?' Hannah asked

innocently, now perplexed by her sister's behaviour.

''Tis disgusting,' Esther pulled her face, distastefully, 'you don't do it that much.'

'Why ever not? We like it!'

'Oh-oh-you poor thing. He's turning you into a woman of the streets' Esther sat down, aghast. 'We don't enjoy that sort of thing. Decent women don't. 'Tis to be endured – a duty only. Oh my, what has he made you do?'

'I...I thought' Hannah stopped abruptly, her cheeks red, her heart thumping wildly as she remembered all too easily the wonder of that first night. And of the love she and Harry shared.

''Tis sinful Hannah.' Esther was visibly shocked. She would have fallen into a faint if she had read Hannah's thoughts.

'I...thought.' Hannah broke off again, unable to find words that Esther might understand. Her feelings were mixed, her thoughts in deep confusion.

'You poor thing,' Esther rose, put a protective arm around the younger woman's shoulders 'I knew he was no good, but to turn a decent soul ... into ... oh, it doesn't bear thinking about.'

'I liked it,' Hannah mumbled, 'it wasn't like you said.'

'Hush!' Esther commanded. 'You didn't like it. You just didn't know. I've heard of his sort before. Pray hard, pray to the Lord for the strength you need. He, in his wisdom, will help you. Next time Harry wants his pleasures – pray. Pray all the time then you will be free of the sin he is leading you in to.'

'It seemed right though.'

'It would, it would,' Esther said soothingly, 'he doesn't know any different. We were brought up proper, knowing the difference between right and wrong. Harry wasn't. How he could treat you in such a vile way I'll never know. And-don't let him bother you too much. 'Tis not at all decent. Besides, you'll most probably be with child by now, especially if he's at you like that.'

'Oh, I hope so, it would be lovely.' Hannah attempted a smile, as thoughts of having her own child made her heart lighter suddenly.

'Hey,' Esther said seriously 'don't let him have his pleasures if you don't get the curse.'

'Why not?'

'Hannah,' Esther shook her head unbelieving at how naïve her young sister could be 'it wouldn't be right if you are carrying. 'Tis a filthy disgusting practice – and besides which – it would harm the brid. Could make it witless. 'Tis a known fact. You go and ask Jenny – what she doesn't know about private matters isn't worth knowing.'

'D'you think I should have words with her?' Hannah asked, anxious to learn what was right and proper for a married woman.

'I would if I were you.' Esther advised 'You'll take more note of what she tells you. And – I wouldn't put up with my husband behaving like an animal. Ask her about that as well. She'll put you right. Then you'll know.'

1877

9

It was the end of December. As the new year rapidly approached, Hannah viewed it with mixed feelings. Times were hard for cotton at the moment and amongst her neighbours, the rumours were flying as to which mill would be next to go. The Middleton Guardian confirmed their gossip, and Hannah read it from cover to cover, making sure she knew the facts. Gossip was gossip. Facts were more important.

'It says here,' she read aloud, 'Lodge Mills are on short time...'

'I know.' Harry butted in with a disapproving scowl. He was rather vexed at her spending a whole penny on the newspaper, that couldn't tell him more than he already knew.

'I should know, I work there don't I?'

'And,' she continued, refusing to be hushed, 'Fieldings in Wood Street are stopped. Eh – listen to this. It says Smiths have packed up altogether.'

'Aye, I've heard that one too' Harry nodded knowingly.

'Bad times.' Her gather muttered unhappily, knowing the grind of searching for work now that he was without it himself.

'It'll pick up again,' Harry said lightly, full of optimism.

'Nay, lad,' Frank shook his head vigorously, 'we're done for. All of us.'

'Father,' Hannah prised herself from the newspaper 'it was far worse in the sixties, as you well know.'

'That's the trouble,' Frank mumbled. Then raising his voice somewhat, let his thoughts tumble out. 'They were bad times and they don't seem that far in the past. There was a lot of suffering for some folks. You youngsters, don't know the meaning of real hard times. You think it's hard now but by God, you know nowt.'

'Aye it was much worse back then,' Hannah said quite cheerfully, refusing to be depressed by their present situation, despite knowing the child inside her could be born into uncertainty.

'You were nought but a child then, lass!' Frank leaned towards her shouting vehemently. 'You don't know the poverty that foreign war brought on us. No cotton, no work. Mills shutting, never to open again. We wanted to work. We would have saved the fly off our clothes and out of our hair if we could've.

'Our lives were poor relief along with thousands of others, all in the same boat. We burnt our few bits of furniture for warmth. We couldn't afford to do otherwise. We were counting ourselves lucky if we ate in more than two or three days a week. Even then it were nowt proper. Barely enough to keep body and soul together. Clemmin' we were. All of us. I can see the same bad times looming. So, don't try and tell me what you don't know about.'

''Tis different this time,' Hannah said cautiously, afraid of her father's sudden outburst.

'Aye and if you saved your coppers, instead of wasting brass on that rubbish,' Harry butted in, 'we might be able to manage alright.' He waved his arm at the newspaper in her hand.

'One penny isn't going to make us any better off.' Hannah said. 'Besides. I can use the paper twice over. It'll d first on the table and then in the privy.'

'We can do without it' Harry insisted, 'I will go unwiped.'

'Aye maybe you can' she folded the paper angrily,' but I won't.'

'You should be arguing over proper things,' her father said suddenly. 'Not things that don't matter. Work is important and what'll you do lad if you come out altogether? Have you given any thoughts to it?'

'Aye, I have.' Harry answered arrogantly 'I'll be trying at the dyeworks up on Wood Street. I'll go now, but I can wait until we move up there. Even work as a carter will do me. I'm not shy of turning my hand to anything,'

'Huh,' Frank mumbled 'so damned cocksure, aren't you lad?'

Hannah and Harry looked at each other, knowing instinctively that it was time to keep quiet and let Frank get on with his brooding.

She felt sorry for her father. He looked worn. Shattered and much older of late. The concern she felt was noticeable. Hannah saw how the life was going from him and would try, against all odds, to keep him as cheerful as possible. But he'd have none of it. If a man couldn't work for his family, then he was much less of a man.

That Harry was still in work and contributing something towards the household, along with Alice and Elizabeth, didn't ease Frank's pain. He was head of the house. But he didn't feel like the master in his own home. It hurt him deeply.

Hannah also knew that, because Harry and she had the chance of a house up at Plundertown, it was worrying Frank too.

Esther had excitedly brought news of the empty house and was putting in a word with the landlord for them. Although Frank had seemed pleased at the time, deep down she knew he wasn't happy. At least while they were living under the same roof, he could keep Harry in check. Once gone? He couldn't bear to think about it. His only consolation was that Esther and Hannah would be neighbours.

Hannah, on the other hand, was more than happy about the chance of her own home. The previous tenants, so she'd heard, had done a moonlight flit. Everyone in the family was out of work and in dire straits. That they had left with a trail of creditors after them was a foregone conclusion.

Moonlighting happened. It was a way of life for some folk. An everyday occurrence in some parts of town. Hannah didn't gloat over the misfortunes of others, least of all on those who hard times befell. The outcome would be to her advantage, but it didn't make her feel any better or worse. She was just happy.

oOo

The following day Frank Adcock complained of feeling a bit off. Hannah, seeing his deathly white face and laboured breathing, fussed constantly over him. Eventually, she insisted he take to his bed until he was feeling better.

Not wishing to alarm her, Frank neglected to tell her of the pain in his chest, refusing to believe it could be anything more than indigestion.

'You can go up to bed,' Hannah clucked, sympathetically, 'I've warmed it up for you.'

'I'll go out to the privy first, lass, don't fuss.' Frank's struggled out of his chair and dragged himself slowly out of the back door. His daughter watched him.

She waited for his return. He had been gone an interminable length of time. Unable to contain her anxiety any longer, she opened the door and called out to him.

There was no answer. No sound from behind the privy door.

Cautiously Hannah ventured out. Her heart was in her mouth, her thoughts confused. Warily she pushed at the privy door. It opened with ease, squeaking noisily.

Frank was still sitting there, his back leaning against the wall. His trousers around his ankles.

'Father?' she spoke, her voice edged with panic.

He didn't move. His eyes, wide open, staring into nothingness.

Backing away Hannah shouted to her neighbour.

'Ada! Oh, Ada! Come quick.'

It was a matter of seconds as the older woman appeared. On seeing Hannah's alarm, she rushed into the privy taking complete charge of the situation.

'Help me get his britches up.' Ada said quickly. She lifted Frank more upright, 'Hurry Up. We must get him inside.'

Hannah dashed to assist. Together they heaved him from the privy, and half carried, half dragged him indoors. They lay him on the floor by the fire.

Hannah got down on her knees and began to rub frantically at her father's cold limbs. Ada, meanwhile, put her ear to his chest, trying without success to detect his heartbeat.

''Please help him,' Hannah beseeched through blurry eyes.

The older woman rose slowly to her feet, her head shaking, and said 'there's nothing to be done, lass.'

'You can't say that!' Hannah sobbed. Unbelieving she pulled and shoved at her father.

'He's gone, Hannah.'

Frank Adcock was dead.

A seizure they said. Or exposure. Exposure more like - was the common gossip. Sat on the privy in the dead of winter, doesn't do. You have to be in and out, sharpish like, not dither about.

There was one comforting factor during the family's bereavement. Frank kept well. Laid out in the parlour in winter was enough to guarantee a well-kept body until the day of the funeral.

Not at all like the height of summer when Alice Adcock had departed this life. In the heat, there was a noticeable swelling of her body, until it reached alarming proportions, along with blackening skin. Her burial was hurriedly brought forward, to enable her to be put underground as fast as humanly possible.

There were the gossips, of course, pretending concern, while quietly churning out their own thoughts. They said poor Alice burst in the coffin on the way to the graveyard, as the cortege travelled along Oldham Road. There were those who swore they heard it. Others, not wishing to be outdone assured all and sundry that they could smell her. And on such a sombre occasion why did the mourners practically run to the burial ground?

There was none of that with Frank. His funeral was conducted in a much more proper fashion, passing off without incident.

10

That's about it, I think.' Hannah surveyed the bundles on the couch. 'There's not much but at least it's all ours.'

'I don't see why you have to move house now. There's no need, not with father gone, There's plenty of room for us all. I do wish you'd think on it, Hannah.' Alice tried to persuade her sister against the move to Plundertown.

'Nay, Alice, we've got the house now and it would be a shame to let it go,' Hannah smiled warmly. 'If we hadn't got it then obviously, we would stay. I know there's room but really, we need a place of our own. Besides, if James comes home, or you or Beth get married, you'll be needing the extra space. Me and Harry would be in the way then. 'Tis for the best really. You can both manage quite well without me, and with the baby on the way...'

'I would prefer you to stay though.' Alice nonchalantly fingered the bundles that Hannah had so lovingly tied up.

'Oh Alice, don't be so daft. I won't be far away. We're not going to the other side of the world you know?' Hannah grinned, amused by her sister, though understanding why there was no immediate need to move to a new house now.

'I just don't see why you need to go,' Alice persisted.

'Oh, go on with you Alice,' Hannah was losing patience, 'I'm very tired and not up to any disagreements with you. Please give it a rest.'

Alice sat down, her face full of sulks.

Hannah ignored her, becoming increasingly concerned by the late hour and Harry's obvious absence. She glanced out of the window, voicing her thoughts. 'Tis way past nine, surely. Where can he be?'

'If you want to go on up,' Alice offered, 'I'll sit and wait for him.'

'Aye, I could do.' Hannah yawned as tiredness threatened to engulf her. 'Maybe I'll wait a bit longer.'

'Nay, go on up, I'll manage' Alice persuaded.

Another hour passed before Harry showed his face. Stumbling first into the privy, then lurching blindly at the back door he almost fell into the house.

'Eh, Harry,' Alice said in hushed tones 'you'll be waking the dead with all that carry on.'

He smiled drunkenly, a leer on his face as he reached towards her.

'You've had more than enough,' she whispered, reaching out to steady him as he weaved past the couch.

His arms went around her and crushed her to him.

Alice didn't protest. She folded herself against him, aware of her beating breast and the tremble in her knees. She twisted her head to look into his eyes and Harry, still with a smile on his face, brought his mouth down to hers, covering her waiting lips.

Alice trembled all the more, caring not for the smell of ale and tobacco that surrounded him but revelling in the warmth and passion of his lips on hers. It was what she yearned for. Having heard the sounds of lovemaking from Hannah's bedroom, the sounds of delight that he'd wrung from her, Alice ached for the same.

She felt his hands slide down to her buttocks and press her savagely against him. Sighing with her own uncontrolled want of the man, Alice gripped him to her fiercely.

'Oh God,' she moaned, 'oh, Harry.'

'Hannah,' he murmured against her ear. Lovingly clasping her tighter, his head swimming, but his desire foremost he moaned again 'Hannah.'

Alice realized in that instant Harry was so drunk he had mistaken her for Hannah. He wasn't making love to Alice at all. He didn't know the difference.

She stayed locked in his embrace, content to let him his hands wander free. She cared not that he assumed she was his wife. For the moment she cared not for anything. Harry was holding her and loving her in the way she'd dreamt he would. It didn't matter to her that they were doing wrong.

Nor did it matter that she was stone cold sober and could stop this madness before it got completely out of hand. She'd yearned for this moment daily and was determined not to let it pass. She wanted to experience all that her sister had.

Harry, his vision hazy, relaxed his hold on her and struggled to focus on the object of his desire. He was feeling uneasy. Something wasn't quite right.

'Oh Harry, hold me' Alice murmured as she felt the sudden change in him.

He peered at her closely. The eyes were the same; the hair as it should be, but he was confused. He could see Hannah. A swift passing vision. Then replaced instantly with the face of Alice.

Shaking his head in confusion he rubbed his eyes with the back of his hands. Harry attempted to coax his sight into showing him what his brain was too befuddled to work out.

It took a couple of seconds, then he saw. The face before him, lovingly gazing up, was that of Alice. It had the desired effect.

He sobered immediately.

Pushing her roughly to one side he muttered 'bitch!'

'Harry,' Alice caught hold of his arm, refusing to be flung aside so easily 'Harry, 'tis alright. I love you.'

'Rubbish!' he spat, angry at the thought she had tricked him so easily. 'Bloody rubbish!'

'But Harry I do' she whispered, hanging onto him with increased fervour.

'Get off.' He snarled, shrugging her off, viciously. 'Get the hell away from me you little bitch.'

'I'll tell Hannah then,' she said, desperately clutching at straws. 'I'll tell her what you did to me.'

In one movement he was in front of her. His hand went out, gripping her tightly by the jaw.

'One word, lass,' he said quietly with a dignified calm, 'just one word.' Then pulling her face to his, he bent, to kiss her with all the warmth and affection he could muster. He didn't want to. But he knew from experience it would be enough to silence the jealous soul. Much better, by far, than to incur her wrath.

'Now,' he whispered, pulling away from her, 'let's not hear any more of this silliness.' He smiled at her, smacking her playfully on the rump, before making his way towards the stairs.

She watched him go. Loving and hating him; both emotions coinciding strongly. Knowing deep in her aching heart that she would never again have the chance to be in his arms. She cursed herself for not having made sure he was drunker than he was. Cursed for having flung herself at him, instead of allowing him to come to her. She could feel the tears form in her eyes, caused by her own frustrations. Shamelessly she let them slide down her cheeks, as she heard the creaking of the bed above her.

Alice knew that the arms she longed to feel around her would now be flung in sheer contentment around her sleeping sister.

1878

11

She lay almost motionless, the single candle flame flickering in the bedroom as she waited for the next inevitable onslaught of pain. Hannah was terribly afraid whilst Harry slept deeply, completely unaware of the fact she had been tossing around for some hours now. Hannah had lit the candle earlier on, hoping that its glow might offer some comfort and delay the moment when she must rouse him from his slumbers.

Counting the pause between pains, Hannah realized that her moments free of discomfort were getting shorter. Ester would have to come quite soon. She would be needed, and only Harry could go.

'Wake up, Harry.' Hannah shook him roughly as another more intense wave of agony swept over her. 'Wake up.'

'Umm,' Harry mumbled sleepily, stirring slightly.

'Please Harry,' she begged. 'Come on you'll have to fetch Jenny and our Esther.'

He jerked awake suddenly and turned to look at her, his face a mask of clear panic as he saw her, pale and writhing alongside him.

Reaching out he touched her lightly and enquired with concern 'are you sure it's going to be now?'

'Yes - yes – yes,' she moaned, her breathing now heavy 'please hurry.'

Harry was out of bed in seconds, frantically dragging his trousers on while trying to find his clogs with his feet.

'Oh!' Hannah let out a surprised sound as she felt a rush of warm wetness flood out from between her legs.

Utter embarrassment enveloped her. She pulled the bed clothes closer around her neck to stop Harry from noticing the soiled sheets.

'Hannah' Harry leaned towards her 'you alright?'

'I feel so ashamed,' she cried, tears springing to her eyes, 'please hurry, go on. Hurry up!'

He turned on his heels and was down the stairs and out of the house at top speed.

As soon as Hannah knew he had gone she threw back the bedding and swung herself carefully out of bed. It was wet now. She tutted, knowing she couldn't lie in it, so she began to strip the bed with fervour. The waves of pain were reaching an intolerable level. But she managed the task in hand and dumped the soiled linen on the floor.

She walked slowly to the window, taking deep breaths. Gripping the windowsill for some support, she listened to Harry banging wildly on Esther's door. He was shouting at the top of his voice. Hannah died a little inside knowing all the neighbours would be roused by the rumpus. The thought caused her acute embarrassment.

She heard Esther shout an answer to Harry and then she saw him run to Jenny's house across the road.

Hannah gripped the windowsill tighter as the whole of her body seemed to shake and tremble with pain. Esther had told her how it would be, and Jenny had assured her that it would be easy. But Hannah was frightened now. She realized nothing could prepare any woman for this experience. Nothing could adequately describe the way she was feeling.

'You should be in bed,' Esther admonished as she appeared at her side and comfortingly threw her arms about Hannah.

'I can't,' the younger woman sobbed, grateful for Esther's presence, 'I wet it.'

'That doesn't matter,' crooned Esther, 'it happens. It's meant to happen. There is no shame in it. Your waters have broke that's all.'

'I'm so afraid,' Hannah was crying, 'it hurts so much.'

'Come on let's get you over to the bed. It'll feel easier if you lie down,' Esther guided her sister back to the bed.

'I don't want to lie down,' Hannah protested.

'You can't stand up, don't be stupid.'

'Ester please don't fuss. It's easier for me being on my

56

feet,' Hannah implored.

'You don't know anything about having babies. We'll be with you and we'll show you, but it will be better for everyone if you lie down,' Esther tried a firmer approach.

Hannah moaned painfully as they reached the bed, then the sounds of Jenny in the kitchen barking orders at Harry floated to her ears.

'She'll be telling him how it's all his fault,' Esther smiled knowingly in the dim light, 'she tells all husbands the same. Mind you, she's usually right.'

Hannah kept her thoughts to herself and began quietly praying. The good Lord would help her in her hour of need, she was sure of it.

Esther, realising that another heavy contraction was in the offing, reached her hands out and, knowing what to feel for, gently ran them over Hannah's stomach. She felt the bulge tighten and harden. Mentally she counted the length of the pain, saying urgently, 'stay there and don't move. I'll get Jenny. She's needed now.'

'Uh hu,' Hannah answered weakly, and as Esther went dashing downstairs she sank to her knees with pain. Gulping desperately for air, an overwhelming desire to push, bore her suddenly to the floor. Involuntary guttural sounds escaped her as Hannah with a fierce strength began to push the infant from her body.

She was vaguely aware of Jenny beside her, clucking at how she should be in bed. But Hannah didn't care anymore. She was certain death was close at hand.

'Hold under her arms, Esther – from behind. Let her lean on you. I've seen it done this way before,' Jenny ordered, completely unflustered.

'Can you manage like this?' Esther asked as she did as Jenny said.

'Yes, no problem,' Jenny smiled. 'We've just got to make sure the little mite doesn't hurt himself on the floor when he drops out.'

'It's going to make a mess of your rug, Hannah,' Esther

said, taking the full weight of her sister against her. Hannah strained noisily.

'Ah, she can make a new one for next time,' Jenny joked dropping to her knees. Then seriously she added 'come on lass get those legs wide open and push as hard as you can into your bottom. You've got to work hard.'

'I'm trying, I'm trying,' Hannah panted angrily. She felt almost torn in two as she silently prayed it would soon be over.

'I can feel the head now,' Jenny beamed, her hands working busily underneath Hannah, 'another good push, lass and you can rest.'

'Push harder,' Esther encouraged, 'come on Hannah.'

'I can't, I can't!' Hannah screamed. 'It hurts too much.'

'You can do it,' Jenny urged. 'You can do it, lass. The head is here, just the body now. Wait for the next pain, take a good deep breath, and then shove as hard as you can. You need to really go for it. You ready?'

Hannah nodded wildly, summoning every ounce of strength within her. And then she pushed and cried out until, with a great surge of relief, and an unexpected squeal of triumph, she delivered her first child into Jenny's waiting hands.

'Good girl!' Jenny laughed out loud, carefully grasping the slippery mite 'you have a lad.'

Swamped with relief and the emotion of the moment, Esther hugged her sister tightly. They both cried tears of happiness as Jenny smacked soundly on the infant's bottom to make him take his first cry.

'Esther you can go and tell Harry now. Mind you with all that carry on up here I think he'll already know.' Jenny smiled. 'Aye and tell him Hannah's done herself mighty proud.

Hannah was now cradling her son close to her body. The still damp bundle of arms and legs, with its pinkish crinkled skin, evoking such strong maternal feelings from Hannah as she rocked him gently. Humming a low tune, she felt all her love and warmth flow out to the tiny body, already forgetting the tremendous hard work and strength used to bring him into the world.

oOo

Harry tip-toed quietly into the bedroom hoping not to disturb Hannah. He took a hurried sidelong look at the infant who was tucked up in the small drawer at the foot of the bed. Immediately he felt an overwhelming sense of pride in seeing his own flesh and blood for the first time.

'Harry?' Hannah whispered tiredly.

'Aye lass,' he felt slightly embarrassed she had caught him in an unguarded moment.

'Shall we call him Edward?'

'Aye, we will. What was good enough for my father is good enough for the child.' Harry agreed. 'Are you alright?'

'Hmmm,' she averted her eyes from his, 'I think so. I'm just dead tired.'

'I was a bit worried for you. Down there – in the kitchen.' Harry shuffled his feet self-consciously.

'I'm sorry.' She felt tears spring to her leaden eyes.

'Nay lass,' Harry sat on the edge of the bed and took her small hand in his. He squeezed it reassuringly. 'I caused you so much pain.'

She didn't answer. He saw the tears run down her cheeks. He reached out to her and wiped face gently with the back of his hand and spoke 'don't cry Hannah, don't cry.'

'You care. You really care.' she said tearfully.

'Aye – but 'tis not for a man to say.' He bent over and kissed her lightly on the lips.

'No, 'tis not done, Harry,' she smiled up at him.

'I can tell you, though, because...' his voice trailed away.

'Because what?'

'Don't matter. You know...' Embarrassed, he let go of

her hand.

'Aye Harry Shaw,' she had suddenly come close to knowing the man. But the moment was past. 'Be off with you, I'm very tired and must get some sleep. I'll not be so heavy eyed when you come home from work.'

'Aye,' he answered sombrely, 'tis almost time for work, the knocker up's been down already.'

'Go on then, don't wait around. Perhaps I'll see you later.'

But she knew as he went off downstairs, that though she would see him - he would not see her – or anything else.

Harold Shaw would be blind drunk.

12

The kitchen was hot and steamy, and Esther pounded furiously on the huge mound of dough on the table. She wiped her arm across her sweating brow, then lifted a corner of her large white apron to remove a streak of flour which she had inadvertently deposited on her nose. Humming lightly to herself, she reached down to the hearth from the warm bowl, then turn automatically upon hearing the click of the latch at the back door.

Harry was framed in the doorway.

'What would you be wanting at this time of day?' Esther asked, putting the dough into the bowl and in the same movement setting it back on the hearth.

'Where's Hannah?' he mumbled, closing the door as he came into the humid room.

'Old Mrs. Taylor died. They laid her out earlier this morning. So, she has taken Jane and the boys along to have a look at her. She was a grand age. Nigh of ninety, I think. 'Tis a shame.' Esther stopped talking abruptly when she realised he was watching her every move. Not just looking, but eying her with a positive leer on his face.

She felt the colour rise to her already. Flushed cheeks she quickly turned her attention to the pans, boiling merrily on the fire before saying, rather sharply 'now, shouldn't you be working?'

'Aye,' Harry answered, slightly amused by the obvious effect he was having on his very staid sister in law. There was a tension building between them. Harry sensed it immediately. He'd come across the feeling many times and enjoyed the consternation he created on such occasions.

'Don't you think that's where you should be?' Esther tried to sound casual and totally unaffected as she raised the large wooden spoon to her lips and tasted her cooking.

He didn't answer as he moved nearer to her, the while eying her with amusement. She wasn't too unlike Hannah, he thought, with her hair scraped back from her face. Slightly taller by an inch or so, a little less weighty – but with the same warm face and brown eyes.

Esther was ruffled and the sight pleased him as he closed in on her. Throwing caution to the wind, he reached forward, encircling her in his arms. In that moment he wanted her.

She struggled for seconds only, then caught sight of his twinkling blue eyes, as he held her fast and pressed himself ever closer. In an instant, before she had time to utter a sound in protest, she felt his lips on hers. The feel and touch of him felt good. Esther was dismayed to find herself shamelessly responding to his ardour.

Feeling weak at the knees, her heart thumping wildly, her better sense prevailed. Esther struggled to free herself from his tight grasp. Slapping at his face, she wiped her lips with the back of her hand and quickly moved to the other side of the table. Her mind raced as she realised what was happening. She had to almost kick herself about the ankles to stop her thoughts running amok. Harry was a fine looking man and she could understand why women wanted him. He had that certain something that she couldn't quite define. Something that had nearly made her succumb to his advances. She had to make herself remember he was Hannah's husband, and that this fleeting moment, in her steamy kitchen, was utter madness.

Taking deep breaths to regain some of her composure, and holding the edge of the table for support, she glared angrily at him.

Harry smiled mischievously as he rubbed the side of his smarting face.

'You'd better get out of here,' Esther managed to find words which sounded right. She wasn't sure that she meant what she was saying but nevertheless had to say it, 'and be sharp about it. We'll have no more nonsense. I don't want you in here again unless Abe is here, do you understand me?'

'Oh, Esther, Esther,' Harry shook his head, chuckling lightly. 'Don't fight it. You're a lovely lass. There's no need to be feared of me.'

'I'm not.' She struggled to remain composed, speaking firmly. 'Now please, go away.'

He advanced towards her again, his arm reaching out to her.

'Go away Harry,' as she slapped his arm from her 'you're despicable.'

'You liked it.'

'No! You make me feel ill.'

'Nay Esther. You liked it and you'd like to know what I'm about.' He grinned broadly, rubbing his groin area, enjoying her discomfort in his actions.

'Oh,' she uttered, shocked completely by his movements, and averting her eyes quickly so as not to witness his unseemly behaviour, added 'you're disgusting.'

'I want you, Esther,' he said throatily, but she felt he was laughing at her.

'Look, Harry, I've seen you with other women. Barely wed and you still can't leave the lasses alone for five minutes. I won't be one – I can resist you.'

'Can you be sure?' Harry turned towards the back door; sure the moment was gone now for any possible conquest.

'Oh yes Harry, I can do without you. But one word of warning before you go. The gossip tongues are wagging about you. I wouldn't want Hannah to hear, her being with child as well. If need be, I'll come down on her side. Every time! There'll be no sympathy from me. You're a rat, Harry. Now get out and don't come here again.' She spoke with grim determination. She had to get the message across to him.

'I'll protect my sister, no matter what.'

She felt a whole lot safer when the latch fell and she watched him go out of the yard. He was laughing, but she felt safer. If circumstances had been different, she might have fallen for the charms of Harry. Thankfully things were as they were and Esther was not one to forget her proper ways - even under such great pressure of temptation.

Pulling herself together, pushing her hair back into place, she dismissed the thoughts in her head. Instead, she turned to her chores and found that before long she was humming again, the incident with Harry forgotten.

Hannah sat down heavily. The pain in her back and lower stomach was draining her. It had started yesterday but she had been too busy much to notice. There had been so much to do, and with the weather being fine for once, she'd washed practically everything she could lay her hands to. It was as she had lifted the tub to empty it into the slop stone sink, that a sharp pain had ripped through her. She'd stopped in her tracks. But as the pain eased to a dull ache, Hannah had dismissed it and carried on with the chores.

But now she couldn't ignore it. It was a signal of something being wrong with the child inside her. And strangely, her feelings on the matter were somewhat mixed.

'Mama, Mama,' two year old Edward, tugged at Hannah, clinging to her knees, and fractiously pulling her for attention.

'Go and play, there's a good lad,' Hannah spoke softly.

He was a beautiful child and loved to be cuddled, but Hannah couldn't summon up enough energy to indulge him. One year old Edith was happily crawling around the flagstone floor, totally occupied with her babyish antics.

'Mama, Mama,' Edward insisted, refusing to relinquish his hold on his mother.

Unable to resist him, Hannah dragged him painfully onto her lap and enclosed him in her arms. The fair-haired child lay his head contentedly against her breast and snuggled close to her familiar warmth. She kissed the top of his head and began to rock him gently, her own discomfort forgotten for a moment.

The click of the latch at the back door, caused her to turn slightly.

'Oh Esther,' Hannah smiled pleased that her sister had called.

'Are you alright?' the older woman enquired. 'You don't look too good, Hannah.'

She came over to Hannah and playfully lifted Edward

from his mother's knee, saying 'Who's a lovely lad then? Does Aunty Esther get a kiss?'

For an answer, the child wrapped his arms tightly around her neck and planted a wet slack-mouthed kiss, near her nose.

'Oooh,' Esther cooed, 'that's lovely. A real treat.'

Still holding him she turned to Hannah and asked 'what is it?'

'I think I'm going to lose the brid,' Hannah, her face drawn in pain, looked to her sister.

'Are you sure?' Esther placed Edward on the floor quickly. 'I best go for Jenny, she'll know.'

'Can you hurry,' Hannah was quite pale.

'Aye, I won't be more than a few minutes,' and Esther rushed from the house.

o0o

'How long have you been having these pains, lass?' Jenny asked with concern, her large frame filling the kitchen.

'Yesterday.'

'Seen anything?'

'No, not yet. But I'm feeling uncomfortable and wet.'

'Right then, let's get you up on that bed. We don't want no haemorrhage.' Jenny rolled her sleeves up, then began to ease Hannah from the chair.

'Why didn't you tell someone yesterday?' Esther asked, worriedly.

'Didn't give it a thought,' Hannah answered as they steered her towards the narrow staircase.

'She's been doing too much,' Jenny said, 'and it doesn't do, especially in the first months. You should know that. Anyway, you're young enough for plenty more, if you do lose this one. Maybe it'll be a blessing. Whichever way it goes, I'll know better when I've had a look at you.'

Hannah liked the over-large Jenny. She was better than any doctor. And always so matter of fact in emergencies.

To her, they were nothing more than the hiccups of everyday life.

'Esther,' Jenny brought her efficiency to the fore, go and get plenty of newspapers. She's losing this one alright. And we don't want too much mess. Not on her lovely clean sheets.'

'I've got some in the house,' Esther dashed from the bedroom, adding as she disappeared, 'I'll drop the childer in at Hilda's next door, so they'll be out of the way.'

'Thanks,' Hannah said, allowing both women to take charge.

'Don't worry your head, lass,' Jenny soothed, 'it'll be all over in no time at all. How far are you gone?'

'About three months I think,' Hannah answered as the midwife busied herself.

'Are you sure? You've not seen the curse for three times?'

'Nay.'

'Worst time, I always say. The ones I've seen who lose at three months, near as many as stillborn.' It was a statement. 'Are you in much pain now?'

'Not too much. I can stand it.' Hannah began to tremble a little, even though the fire was roaring up the back of the chimney.

'Some say tis worse than giving birth,' Jenny clucked, 'but tis not the same for everyone.'

'Aye, I'd heard,' Hannah moved uncomfortably, then felt an unmistakable warmth ooze from between her legs. 'Jenny. I think something is happening.'

The fat woman quickly attended to Hannah, then peering closely in a very professional fashion, said, 'don't panic, it's going to be alright. Some of it has just come away. You've not been at the penny royal, have you?'

Hannah shook her head, then felt the tears spring to her eyes. She didn't know why. Couldn't explain why she should feel so depressed by what was happening to her. It was, as Jenny said, probably a blessing in many ways.

Esther appeared in the doorway, arms full of newspapers.

'Hilda gave me some, will it be enough?' she asked breathlessly.

'Aye,' Jenny answered, 'now if we spread them out underneath her, quite thick, I can see about raising the foot of this bed. We don't want to take any risks of haemorrhaging. Can you get some water on the boil, Esther, because I'll need plenty?'

oOo

Hannah Shaw lost Harry's third child just before teatime. Jenny and Esther between them, took over completely, making sure there was no risk to Hannah.

They poured hot sweet tea down her throat, to combat any shock, and cleaned her up with clean cloths and hot water. Inspecting all that had expelled from Hannah's insides, and clucking with satisfaction at a job well done, they burnt the resultant mess on the fire.

'I'll pop in later to see how you are,' Jenny said sympathetically when there was nothing else left to do. 'Now no getting out of bed, until I say so. And don't let that husband of yours anywhere near you. Or you'll catch straight off.'

'Thank you, Jenny,' Hannah managed a weak smile, ''tis good to have you around.'

'It's what I'm good at,' Jenny turned to Esther 'and I've never had any fevered mothers in all my years of attending. Shows how clean I am lass.'

'Where would any of us be without you?' Esther smiled gratefully, as Jenny made her way to the top of the stairs.

'Mind she tells Harry to keep off of her,' her voice dropped to a whisper, 'she's lost the mite, cause she's having them too close. I know what these men are, but bedroom doors can be clocked.'

'I'll remind her,' Esther said, used to the way in which

Jenny blamed every woman's ailment or complaint on the menfolk.

'Be sure she does. That's if he comes home.'

o0o

Harry wasn't too pleased when he came in from work, to find Esther busy feeding her children and his own – at his table. It wasn't done to have anyone in at mealtimes, even if they were relations.

'Where's Hannah?' he asked gruffly as he sat down and began to loosen the laces on his clogs.

'Up in bed, Harry,' Esther answered, as she laid a plate for him 'she lost the brid.'

'So that's why you're here then?' he got up to sit himself at the table.

'Aye, I've been here most of the day,' Esther piled his plate with the remaining hotpot, 'but I shall be off soon as you've eaten, so there's no need to fret. Abe will be home soon.'

'You make this?' his mouth full.

'Aye.'

'Not bad. Not bad at all.'

He didn't speak to her again. Silently he cleared his plate, eyeing the children between mouthfuls, then scraping back his chair and rising without further ado' disappeared upstairs.

'How are you lass?' he asked without much concern.

'I shall be alright,' Hannah answered quite brightly. She could see how tired he was and understood his intolerance to illness and weakness. It upset his way of life, and anything that did was a nuisance to him. 'I'm blood tired,' he yawned as if to confirm her thoughts, then added, 'best ask Esther to put the childer to bed.'

'I'll ask her when she comes up. Jenny might pop in later – to make sure I am doing as I'm told.'

'Oh, God, no' he mumbled angrily.

'She won't stay long. Besides, she is a good woman and we'll more than likely need her again,' hoping to steer him away from his bad humour.

'S'pose we will. But she's a right one.'

'Aw, c'mon, she's not that bad.'

'Always having a go at us men. She'd be better off if she kept her mouth shut and her thoughts to herself.'

'Ah, that's just Jenny.'

'When will you be up again?'

'Depends what Jenny says,' Hannah smiled at him. Harry, in turn, was yawning, widely. 'Go and have a nap, you'll feel better than.'

'Aye, I think I will.' He turned to leave the room, then as an afterthought, added mischievously 'we can soon have another.'

'We probably will, Harry, I've no doubts on that,' she sighed knowing for certain that her loss would soon be replaced.

14

'Ooh, but it's all go,' Jenny said breathlessly, having just met up with Esther on Wood Street. 'Old Fitton's on his way out, that's where I'm off now. Doing everything under him, he is. A sure sign if ever I saw one. And Annie Smith's due in a couple of days.

''Tis brass in your pocket though,' Esther smiled as Jenny puffed and panted in an exaggerated fashion, 'and work that's to your liking.'

'Aye but it takes it out of you, rushing here – rushing there, leaves me no time to think.'

'We'd be lost without you. A godsend you are,' Esther praised her, lavishing her with the credit she was due, all the while keeping an eye on Charles and Abraham, who were running in circles around them both.

'Full of it, aren't they,' Jenny laughed, then added, 'where's your Jane then?'

'I've left her with Hannah, keeping an eye on her two. You know what she's like, our Hannah? Not one for lying a bed, even when she should,' Esther explained, concerned.

'Aye, I know alright. There's nowt much will keep her off her feet. But she should take heed. It's in years to come, then it'll all come home you know. Problems with the innards like. Then that husband of hers will be in a right old pickle. Makes a mockery of her, he does. A laughingstock. A right laughingstock.'

'I know. I know,' Esther sighed in agreement.

'Should be hung, drawn, and quartered. Indeed, he would be if I had my way. Neither use nor ornament. 'Tis a shame she's lumbered,' Jenny said heavily 'but then again, there's worse than him around. Much worse.'

'Ooh I know,' Esther agreed readily, knowing that whatever Jenny had to say about Harry Shaw, would be completely true.

'Don't go saying I've told you, but,' Jenny moved closer

to add, in not much more than a whisper 'I saw him with a lass only the other night.'

'Oh no' Esther exclaimed, visibly taken aback.

''Tis right I did. Bold as brass he was. Staggering out of the alehouse. Dusty Miller it was. This floozy on his arm, with not a care in the world as to who might see. I wouldn't have seen them, only I stayed a bit longer at old man Fitton's, with him dying anytime. It's best I keep dropping in.'

'He makes me so angry, Jenny,' Esther was more than a little vexed, 'but I can't tell her, she'd never forgive me. We never did take to him, but she wouldn't be told.'

'Aye, and now she's made her bed.'

'I help all I can, but what else can I or any of us do?'

'I'll give you a little tip,' Jenny said, low, making sure Esther's children were out of earshot 'mind you don't go telling other womenfolk though. Or I'll be out of pocket, right enough.'

'I don't gossip, as you rightly know,' Esther assured her.

'If Hannah shoves a lump of lard, dipped in flour, up her insides. You know – her privates like – just before he takes his pleasures, it'll stop her catching so often.' Jenny spoke quickly lest any passers-by should overhear.

'Ooh Jenny I've never heard of that one,' Esther grimaced.

'Can't say if it works though. In my line of business, I get to hear all sorts. And some right queer things too. It seems to be popular with the floozies. Mind you I don't attend the likes of them. I'm quite particular. And wouldn't want troubles from my regulars.'

'Umm' Esther pondered, 'it's worth a try.'

'I should think anything to stop her falling like she does, is worth having a bash at. It can't hurt any, being natural things, thought it might be a bit distasteful and messy, I should think.' Jenny laughed, nudging Esther as another thought crossed her mind, 'shifting a man's britches off the end of the bed doesn't work either.'

'Ah it's an old tale is that one,' Esther laughed, enjoying Jenny's forthright humour, 'been going since the year dot. Like I used to believe if a chap smiled at me across the street that were it.'

'Aye 'tis funny the things we were told,' Jenny let out a strong belly laugh, then added, more seriously 'anyway tell her to try it out, and time alone will tell us if it works.'

'Aye I will' Esther said. 'I might even be tempted to try it for myself.'

'I knew it! I knew it!' Jenny threw her arms up in mock vexation 'doing myself out of brass.'

'I doubt it' Esther assured her, then turning to her boys, now tired of running around and sitting quietly on the kerb edge 'c'mon, let's make tracks for home, Aunt Hannah will be thinking we've got lost.'

'Aye, I's best be off as well. The old man will be dead and buried before I get there.'

'Tell him I asked after him' Esther said, clasping the boys' hands, one either side of her.

'I will, Esther – and mind that sister of yours does as she's told.' And with that Jenny turned away, heading down Wood Street to attend to more pressing matters.

oOo

Harry came into the kitchen still fumbling with the flies on his trousers and muttering, 'blue bottles! Can't you do something about them? Couldn't sit there for long with them buggers all over me.'

'I can't do much about them – with this hot weather they're into everything. Besides, I'm doing my best.' Hannah answered as she thrust a pot of tea into his hands. The thought that it would be a pleasure to throw it over him, quickly passed.

'Stinks it does.'

'It's not my fault,' she commented, 'everyone's privy is the same just now. Should think there'll be some fever

73

around before long.'

'Don't want any fever in this house.' Harry was busy filling his pipe. 'Where's the taper?'

'Can't you have your tea first?'. Hannah was dishing up his tripe.

'Don't mither lass, I'll eat when I'm ready.'

Showing her displeasure, Hannah slapped the tripe noisily onto his plate, banged it down on the table, and covered it with a clean piece of linen.

'You need to wash too,' she said quite calmly. 'The privy and you make a good pair.'

Edward and Edith sat quietly, eating their tea, their eyes watching the adults carefully. Even at such a tender age, they could sense all was not well.

'Watch your mouth woman!' Harry bellowed, causing both children to sit rigid and open-mouthed.

'There's no need for shouting.' Hannah glared at him.

'I'll shout in my house and bugger the neighbours,' his voice purposely grew louder with each word uttered. Hannah went to close the back door, which had been left open because of the heat of the day. They'd often heard loud rows from the neighbours, and she knew they'd all have their ears pricked in gleeful anticipation of a squabble at the Shaw's.

'Leave it!' Harry barked.

Undeterred, Hannah closed the door. He could please himself what he did but she needed to retain some decorum. Hannah Shaw was a cut above the rest and any noisy altercation would only serve to lower her social standing in the local community stop.

'Get your tea Harry,' Hannah said boldly 'And then be off to ale house.'

Harry tapped out his pipe and seated himself at the table, opposite quivering children. They watched their father intensely looking for the smallest sign that it was their turn next.

'And before you go,' Hannah ventured daringly, 'leave

me some coppers.'

The words had barely left her lips when she felt the sharp stinging blow to her cheek.

Harry growled 'hold your tongue woman.'

Edith, frightened by the sudden turn of events began to wail and Hannah automatically moved

'Leave her be!' Harry caught hold of Hannah

'You scared the mite,' she pulled away from him and immediately picked the child up. 'There, there it's all right now don't cry.'

'What's all this about?' he asked, not understanding her mood.

'I can tell you. Oh yes, I can tell you' she hissed at him as she continued soothing the sobbing Edith 'but you better keep your voice down. What I've got to say isn't for the ears of anyone.'

'Out with it lass,' Harry demanded.

'I had a visitor today,' she delivered the words as calmly as she could, 'from over Jumbo way.'

'Bloody liar!' Harry shouted, immediately on the defensive.

'Oh no, Harry. I don't lie and you know it.' She felt a sudden rush of hate for him and it showed on her face. 'We don't deserve any of this from you.'

Violently sweeping his arm across the table, in pure rage, Harry knocked most of the crockery to the floor, including his untouched meal. Hannah put the child down and proceeded to gather the broken mess into a pile. 'Go on, wreck the house while you're at it. It's only me who has to clean it up.'

'It's what you're born for, woman.'

'Hah! How any woman can take to you I'll never know.'

'You did.'

'I should have had more sense!' Hannah spat the words at him. She was angrier now than he had ever known.

Without warning, he lunged at her. She automatically backed away from him. But catching her by the shoulders, he gripped her fiercely.

'Who told you these lies?' he demanded, shaking her roughly.

'You don't know?' Hannah was incredulous. 'You really don't know? How many are there, Harry? How many? Tell me how many more?'

Again, she felt his hand as he struck wildly at her face.

Daring him, she deliberately turned the other cheek, saying viciously 'go on – and again. Don't stop now Harry. Beat me black and blue if it makes you feel better – if it absolves you of your wrongdoings, then, by all means, carry on.'

Shaking with rage he looked into her angry eyes, sorely tempted to hit her again and again. No woman had ever spoken to Harry in this way before and he didn't like it. He wanted to hit out blindly until he'd quietened her. The truth had finally come home. It was under his very roof, coming from the mouth of his wife - and he was devastated. He couldn't ask her to understand. It just wasn't done. the master of the house came and went without question and here she was, knowing everything and boldly tackling him about it.

'Keep your mouth shut,' Harry spat the words at her, 'because believe me, I could so easily kill you.'

'You think I didn't know about those women?' Hannah persisted, sick to her stomach. Sick with fear at the thoughts of what he might do to her. But with a fierce determination, she stood her ground. 'You've disgraced us – disgraced this family. You and your filthy disgusting ways.'

The rage flared and, unable to contain himself any longer Harry, hit her hard - banging her head against the wall, and without saying another word he dug into his trouser pocket and threw a halfpenny at her. Swearing under his breath he turned on his heel and slammed out of the back door rattling the tin bath with such force that it clanged deafeningly to the floor.

Edward ran to his mother and threw his arms tightly

around her heavily skirted legs, while Edith shrieked and wailed at full blast. The pain in Hannah's head pounded unceasingly, whilst her tears rolled silently down her face to join the trace of blood oozing from her mouth.

She gripped the kitchen table for support her dazed body shaking - her mind in complete turmoil wondering what was to become of them.

15

'You shouldn't have done it, Lucy Deakin,' Harry Shaw sat in the kitchen of the none too clean house and glared angrily at the older woman.

'What was I to do?' Lucy implored. 'You didn't pay enough. You with the fine wife – a nice house, good clothes. What did you expect us to do? A man has to pay for his mistakes.'

'I've been paying more than enough,' Harry said angrily.

'No, you haven't. I've lost a working lass because of you. And in her place, I get another mouth to feed.' Lucy hissed.

'You shouldn't have gone to Hannah.'

'No, you should have kept your hands to yourself. Mucking about with my Sal, and her being such a young lass. Not decent it ain't. Not right,' Lucy persisted.

'She was willing. There was no forcing her you know?' Harry's distaste of the unkempt woman showed on his face. The house didn't smell too good either and he was breathing with difficulty in the rancid room.

'That's as maybe but you are a married man. You should've known better and not took advantage' she smiled revealing uneven rotting teeth.

'Say what's to be done. Say what's on your mind.'

'You take the mite!' she said, triumphantly. 'Then you don't have to pay me no more.'

'I can't do that, and you know it.' The sight of her mouth, filled with brown stumps, was sickening him. 'Besides, I couldn't explain to Hannah.'

'You don't need to tell what she already knows.' Lucy was feeling pleased with herself now. 'Just tell her to come and pick it up whenever she fancies. Maybe tonight.'

Lucy had been squeezing Harry for money ever since Sal had been taken by the childbirth fever, but now she'd had enough. With eight mouths to feed already and a lost wage, she didn't need the extra burden.

'I can't ask Hannah to do it' Harry looked at her in complete disgust.

'It's your bastard anyway – and if you don't, well it could just end up in the canal.'

'I won't let you do that! Have you no heart woman?'

'Hearts don't feed childer, lad.' The woman was evil, he was sure.

'And where was your heart when my Sal needed it?'

'I told you, I didn't force her. Her legs opened up like yonder lock gates.' Harry was becoming bored with the whole thing now.

'Don't you talk dirty about my Sal.'

'Come off it, Lucy – she were no angel.'

'Not like Hannah' the woman cackled, rocking back and forth in her own private world of humour.

'Leave her out of it. If she's going to take this brat off your hands, I'd watch what you say. You're not fit to lick her boots.' Harry scraped back his chair and rose to signal his intentions of leaving.

'You'd best leave some money, so I can feed it.'

'You'll get nowt else off me until I've spoken to Hannah. And if she takes it tonight there won't be so much as a farthing in it for you.'

'Make it quick then Harry. I don't want the little bastard around longer than I have to.' Lucy was smiling again, once more flashing her disgusting teeth at him.

'On condition that you'll keep your mouth tight shut about any of this' Harry warned vehemently. 'Hannah's suffered enough through you. Make any noises at all and I'll come looking for you and shut you up for good.'

'Threatening me?' Lucy tutted.

'Aye if that's what you want to call it. Just don't try me. Whatever you do, don't try me.'

oOo

16

Seeing Hannah in total disarray, broken pots on the flag stones, blood at the edge of her mouth, and the children bewildered and frightened had Ester fuming and raging. The audacity of the man! As the two women cleaned up the kitchen, Hannah, between sniffles, related the goings on which had led up to the inevitable outcome.

'He's dented the bath,' Esther said angrily as she hung it back on the door. Then standing with legs apart and hands on hips she reached a decision. 'We'd best get our Alice and Beth up here and see what we can do about him. Disgusting he is.'

'Do we have to?' Hannah wiped her eyes with the back of her hand, pushing away a stray wisp of hair from her face 'I'll die of shame.'

'They're family Hannah. And besides, it's not your shame.' Esther was firm. 'Our Beth won't be much use, but the more of us here, the better.'

oOo

When Harry returned, that was what he found to greet him. The sight of all four sisters united against him. He felt their strength as one accord, as silently they watched his every move, glaring with icy contempt.

Defensive, wanting to show that he was master in his own home, he barked 'I want them out of here!'

'Not until we've discussed your dallying,' Esther piped up, completely unafraid of him. 'Things have to be said.'

'None of your bloody business!' he grunted, noting the young Beth's attractive qualities. She caught his eye, then blushing profusely, in a way more fitting to Hannah, quickly averted hers.

'Ah, but it is,' Esther persisted 'we're family and whatever concerns Hannah, concerns us.'

'Meddling. That's it – plain meddling.'

'Hannah needs us,' Alice was vehement 'and that's how it'll be.'

'What's up? She lost her tongue then?' a wry smile spread across his face. Glancing across at her he noted her swollen lip. A sudden feeling of guilt washed over him. He was ashamed to have taken it out on her.

'No, they've come to help sort out this mess,' Hannah answered. ''Tis no use you and me trying to talk, you'll only hit me again.'

'Aye and keep it up Harry and...' Alice snarled.

'Sod off!' he barked, cutting her off mid-sentence. 'There'll be no more trouble from Lucy Deakin.'

'You've sorted it out then?' Esther asked in disbelief.

'Aye. Of a fashion'

Harry's head was now bowed. He couldn't face Hannah.

'How?' Esther demanded, her patience running thin. 'C'mon – how?'

'Hannah can have the child,' his head came up, his eyes fixed on his wife. 'Best pick it up this night. Maybe after dark. It'll end up in the cut if you don't.'

The sisters gasped, open mouthed in astonishment. Esther, the first to recover, blurted out 'my God what do you think she is?'

'She's my wife' Harry answered, suddenly quite unconcerned as to their thoughts on the matter 'and she'll do as I say.'

'Oh my!' Alice cried out, shocked, throwing an arm around Hannah's shoulders. Beth, blushed, her hand rising quickly to stifle a cry of disbelief from her lips.

'The woman won't throw it in the cut - would she?' Esther asked, unsure.

'Aye and she wouldn't think twice about it either,' Harry assured them.

'Pray to the Lord for forgiveness, Harry Shaw!' Esther raged.

Harry looked to Hannah and saw the complete look of

disgust and a fleeting glimpse of hatred on her face. He didn't know what else you could say to her. And he couldn't admit how wrong he'd been. Lord – he knew how much he had wronged her. But it was done, and nothing would change anything.

Hannah wavered for a moment.

Then slowly, as if reading his thoughts, and measuring her words carefully, she said with a sharp edge to her tongue 'Somebody will forgive him. 'Someone, somewhere, will.'

oOo

Edith and Edward were well tucked up in bed as Hannah set about the task of cleaning the child. She'd boiled water and arranged bits of clothing on the maiden in front of the fire to air. The drawer that she had used previously for her children, she lined in sheeting, ready to accept the infant.

Alison Beth went over to Lucy Deakin's straight away. relieved to be out of Harry's way and happily hoping to avert a possible scandal. They hadn't waited until darkness fell but brazenly done the deed in full light.

Both would have been quite content to take the child in themselves but Hannah had insisted that the burden was hers to bear remaining a constant reminder to Harry.

He watched Hannah has she lovingly washed the grime from the child. Cooing and making the motherly sounds that calmed the agitated mite. She loved children and the way in which she handled him showed it. With some of the muck off it, Harry thought *it looks more like what it should.*

'You going out?' Hannah asked, not even glancing up at him. Finding any words to say to him at this point was an ordeal in itself.

'Maybe' he answered, 'thought I'd sit a while.'

'With another mouth to feed, the coppers will come in handy.' She spoke low, carefully drying the waif.

'Expect so,' Harry mumbled, knowing that a few good

jugs of ale were beckoning.

'What name shall he have?'

'George is his name.' Harry felt utterly guilty at having to proffer the child's name. It was as if he was admitting to what he'd done. And as he watched her rocking the infant gently, he wondered about her thoughts. Her face expressionless, he could sense her mind was weaving some tale to silence the nosey neighbours. He couldn't take a guess, but he knew Hannah would hold her head high, come what may, and would in time inform him.

'Not George,' Hannah spoke suddenly, 'Harry it'll be.'

'As you say, lass,' he agreed easily. 'As you say.'

He watched a while longer, not understanding her quiet acceptance of the situation. Then reaching for his cap and tapping out his pipe in the hearth he muttered that he'd just be off for a drop of ale.

Hannah said nothing. She just eyed him, somewhat vexed, but let him go. She hoped there'd be enough guilt on his shoulders to keep him away from other women - at least for tonight anyhow. She was relieved to have him out of the house, the tension being unbearable, and she needed some time alone to think. Time to work out how best to cope, not only with Harry but the children as well.

She'd heard details about Harry as she'd passed many a gossiping group of women standing idly on the street corners, with nothing better to do. Even when out shopping down in Market Place she'd detected whispers and sidelong glances from all sides as she frugally eked out the coppers Harry had given her. There was only once that she'd hit back when the voice of Edie Dyson carried further than she liked, and Hannah quite vexed had told the interfering busybody, in no uncertain terms, to mind her own business.

Apart from that, she'd managed to ignore all comments and put it down to jealousy. There were many who had good reason to be jealous where Hannah was concerned. Harry was a fine looking man. Quite handsome really and the Shaw household was run with him as the complete master. Hannah's putting up with his drinking habits was the envy of many, but Harry worked hard for his pleasure and she wasn't one to complain unless she was going short of food and money.

Her home was spotlessly clean, the flagstone floor scrubbed regular, the front step always well donkey stoned, And all clothing made by Hannah - oh yes they had every reason to be envious of such a capable woman.

This visit from Lucy Deakin had made Hannah realise just how blind she had been. How, smug and secure in her own well-ordered life, she had failed to recognise that where there's smoke there's bound to be fire.

The dirty unkempt creature from over Jumbo away had made sure that Hannah knew exactly what the man was up to and had demanded extra money into the bargain. Shocked almost numbed beyond belief, Hannah had listened to the tale as the full picture emerged in colourful detail.

The young Sally Deakin fell easily for the charms of the very bold, obviously irresistible Harry Shaw, something that Hannah understood. On night-time trips to the alehouses he frequented, Harry had done much more than quietly sup ale. There were plenty of back alleys and fields in and around Middleton for the squalid copulation which resulted in the bastard child.

Lucy had assured Harry that all the penny royal and turpentine she could lay their hands couldn't shift the brat. Not even the controlled fall downstairs had made any odds. By the time she tried everything they could think of, it was too late to do ought else. It was up to Harry to see them right. Realising the folly of his deeds he'd paid mother and daughter throughout, hoping that nothing would come to light.

But poor Sally died within hours of the birth - presenting Harry with a lusty son. A greedy young thing he was too. Lucy, seeing a way out, sparsely fed the child hoping it too would follow its mother to the grave, but it was not to be. The child was strong enough to survive Lucy's cruel treatment. A born fighter. A Shaw in every sense.

Not wanting to keep the mite any longer and knowing for certain that it would, without doubt, have a much better life in the Shaw home, Lucy had, without conscience, confronted Hannah. She didn't care who was hurt or what problems her confrontation might produce.

Hannah didn't argue with the woman, she just accepted what was said. Then cried buckets when she was finally on her own again. Tears not only of hurt but because of how unjust life seemed to be and of the way in which Harry had let her down. The tales of scandal that she'd so easily dismissed, in their courting days, had come home to her like a smack in the mouth.

As she sat and thought, turning everything over, again and again, the night closed in. The neighbourhood sounds drifted to her, breaking her reverie. A dog barked somewhere. Sounds from next door penetrated the wall and Hannah could hear raised voices. She sighed upon recognising the harsh noise of argument and tried to close other people's problems from her mind.

She had enough troubles of her own.

She devised a suitable tale concerning the child's arrival. One that would keep the gossips at bay. She'd raise it as her own, supposedly come from a cousin down Manchester way after having been left an orphan. The neighbours would ooze sympathy - but whether or not they'd believe her didn't matter. None of them ever ventured that far out of Middleton, anyway, so proving her wrong or a liar would be trifle difficult.

Her married brothers need never know the truth. Not that she saw anything of them these days. What with Ben and James living over Scarborough way and Frank up in Westmorland there was no one to worry about.

Satisfied with her plans, but not satisfied with Harry at

all, she decided that this night she wouldn't be waiting up for him to come home. She'd show him that he couldn't keep taking advantage. Show him that her life wasn't going to revolve around him.

Hannah Shaw would have to be a much stronger woman if she were to put up with Harry and his ways.

'Humph!' she muttered to herself as she lightly climbed the stairs, 'and how long will it last, if I do indeed find the strength?'

17

The house was quiet when Harry finally stumbled home. The interior darkness hit him as soon as he was through the door. He knew immediately that Hannah was in bed.

Blindly lurching and banging against the furniture, he manoeuvred himself towards the stairs and attempted the steep climb. Having negotiated the first few, Harry almost fell backwards. Swearing and cursing he decided it would be better to drag himself to the top on his knees.

Crashing into the bedroom, still on all fours, he began fumbling under the bed, until after what seemed like an age he triumphantly pulled out the Jerry. Using the edge of the bed for support, Harry stood up shakily and tore at his pants until, with a sign of satisfaction, a hot stream of urine splashed noisily into the receptacle.

Hannah didn't move at all and he guessed she was feigning sleep. No one could sleep through the noise he was making. Even the infant was snuffling and moving somewhere in the room. Bending cautiously, he put the Jerry back down and pushed it back under the bed with his foot – sloshing some of its content onto the floor.

Laboriously, Harry began to disentangle himself from his clothes. Clothes that suddenly wanted to stay firmly on his body. So, flopping drunkenly on the bed and trying to contain his laughter as the simplest task seemed impossible, he tried to undress in a sitting position. He found that his feet wouldn't come nearer to his hands, to rid himself of his clogs. So, with a grim determination to win, in what was now turning into a battle, he tore at his clothing, dropping them into a heap on the floor and finally kicked off the offending footwear. Then belching loudly, he roughly threw himself onto the bed.

Moving close to Hannah he encountered the bolster. Anger began to tear through his ale soaked mind. Making more noise than was necessary, he dragged at the offending obstacle until he had successfully manhandled it to the floor.

Pleased with his achievements, he reached towards Hannah and immediately felt her warmth. She had her back to him, but undeterred he moved closer until her clean smell pervaded his nostrils. She smelled good, he mused. Warm and clean. There were no stale tobacco and ale odours about her. No unwashed whorish stink about his woman.

Flinging his arm across her, his hand came to rest on her full breast, causing an instant reaction in his loins. Thrusting his growing erection against her buttocks, his hand tightened on her breast. Without warning, Hannah moved suddenly from his unwanted advances and turned quickly on her stomach.

'Playing games with Harry?' he chuckled low, and in a single movement, climbed atop of her and began tugging at her nightdress.

'Get off!' she hissed between clenched teeth, not wanting to make any sounds that might wake the sleeping children.

Unhearing – uncaring – Harry continued pulling at her night attire until it reached her waist. She was powerless to stop him. He had her pinioned face down.

'Turn over lass. Or I'll take you this way. The way the whores like it.'

Hannah began to weep. He could sense it.

'Turn over' he ordered.

This time, sobbing quietly, she turned, and Harry lifted himself slightly to allow her to face him.

'That's better, lass,' he smiled to himself as his hand reached lower until he found the warm softness between her thighs. She was incredibly soft to touch, and Harry felt his own desires become more urgent, even though she lay rigid and unyielding.

'Open your legs' he rasped as he prodded his erection against her.

Hannah was still sobbing as she did his bidding, but he

ignored her and lunged his hips forward several times until with a sigh of satisfaction he reached his goal. Sliding into the liquidity that was to appease the throbbing in his loins, Hannah began to quietly pray.

'Stop it, lass,' Harry said breathlessly, then gripping her jaw roughly he repeated 'stop it! You enjoy it, like our wedding night. Just lay there and let Harry pleasure you.'

He thrust hard into her, alternating between fast and slow, while Hannah tried to resist the feelings that were stirring within her. She tried for what seemed like hours. She tried, as the bed groaned and creaked to the rhythm of Harry's unceasing pounding. But slowly her resolve weakened until her moans began to blend in with the sounds in the room and she yielded to him.

Tearing at her restricting nightdress he released her breasts, baring the whole of her body to him. Breathlessly he urged her on. She matched his urgency without question until her writhing reached their peak,

'Oh Lord, oh Lord. Harry' she almost screamed.

Clamping his hand firmly across her mouth to quieten her flood of ecstasy, he emptied himself into her. With the grunt of a man whose lustful passions have been spent, he lightly kissed the woman beneath him, lingered for a moment to touch the swollen lip caused by him earlier in the day, then pulled away from her.

'G'night' he mumbled, then sleepily turned his back to her.

Hannah lay quietly, almost stiff, still on her back with her nightdress torn and in disarray. She didn't dare to move, not even to pull the bedclothes up to cover her modesty. The tears sprang easily to her eyes as she realised what he'd done to her was unforgiveable. He'd treated her like a common street woman. Made her enjoy his animal lust, caring not for her feelings.

With a shudder she carefully, so as not to disturb the now snoring Harry, slid out of bed. Locating the Jerry she squatted over it, added her urine to Harry's, and with her fingers frantically tried to scoop out the mess he'd put inside her.

Feeling torn apart with the guilt she clambered back into bed and wept. And prayed well into the night – because she could not come to terms with the fact that she had enjoyed that which should, to a woman of her upbringing, be endured in sufferance only.

1881

18

Harry walked in to utter confusion, and immediately wished he'd lingered in the alehouse. His home was no comfort when other folks were there. Home wasn't much comfort at the best of times.

Edward and Edith came towards him, gleeful smiles on their young, innocent faces and began tugging boisterously at his trouser legs. Patting Edith's head affectionately and tickling Edward just under his chin, he steered himself with difficulty towards his chair, dragging both children along with him. Their peals and shrieks of laughter reflected their delight, as they hung on to their father.

Esther appeared then the young Harry in her arms. She seemed flustered, with hair awry and completely at odds with herself.

Seeing Harry, she let forth an angry torrent. 'So, you've come home have you? Not before time either. How could you go off for days like that, leaving Hannah sick with worry?'

Harry lit his pipe and sucked contentedly, before saying 'Go to hell.'

'Scum' she retorted, her face flushed, her patience wearing thin. 'Tis about time you grew up and took on some of your responsibilities.'

'Go home Esther' Harry hissed through teeth that were still holding his pipe fast, 'bugger off.'

'Aye, I will be doing, soon as I've finished with Hannah. By God man, you've not even asked after her,' vexed. Her voice conveyed all the contempt she felt for him.

'What ails her?' he tussled Edward's hair as the child clambered up onto his knee.

'You have another daughter' she said brusquely, before adding, cruelly 'and a dead son.'

He didn't turn to look at her, didn't show that he'd heard, just carefully shifted Edward from his lap.

Presently he spoke 'I shall go up in a minute.'

'Don't bother. She won't be wanting to see you, Harry. That's the last thing she'd want' Esther said with fierce conviction. 'Hannah says you are the cause of her lost child. The poor lass is beside herself, full of grief and suffering for the soul.'

'You're talking soft.' He rose, stretching to his full height.

'Nay Harry, 'tis your doing from what I've heard in this house today. Using her in such a despicable way' Esther spat venomously. 'She could take a fever now and if aught happens to her then you'll have the good Lord to reckon with.'

'Sod off' Harry brushed her roughly to one side as he made his way towards the stairs.

o0o

Esther was right. Hannah wouldn't speak to him. Wouldn't acknowledge his presence in the room. She deliberately turned her face from him, when he reached forward to brush the tears from her red-rimmed eyes.

He glanced at the child sleeping peacefully in the drawer at the bottom of the bed but saw no sign of the other.

He asked her, but she remained tight-lipped. Angry he stormed from the bedroom, determined to get an explanation of Hannah's behaviour from Esther. Something Esther was more than pleased to do.

When Hannah's pains began, it had all seemed right enough. Jenny said all along that Hannah was carrying at least two. Hannah herself had an inkling there might be.

The first, a girl, entered the world without problems. Then came the agony as Hannah laboured long and hard in a fierce attempt to push the second child from her body. The difficulties became apparent when the infant's legs appeared first. To all present, it seemed as though it took hours longer and through it, Hannah cried out; damning

Harry to hell for what he'd done to her. Treating her as a wanton, making her enjoy sinful pleasures of the flesh until the good Lord had repaid her in this sad way.

Jenny had clucked and tutted with much sympathy and understanding in all the right places, not in the least surprised by the revelations of the confined woman. It was part of the job listening to the ramblings of a distressed woman during a long and difficult birth. Jenny wouldn't have expected anything else as she gently pulled at the child's legs, hanging from Hannah.

After a while, the midwife knew instinctively the child would be dead. It was taking too long by far and she hadn't been able to secure a hold on the cord.

The brid was pulled from Hannah, as the farmer would assist the birthing of a calf. It was the only thing she could do to ease the torture and the pain for her. As the infant, limp and blue, having been strangled by its own cord was wrested from its mother – Hannah in a state of delirium let forth a string of verbal offerings.

Esther tried to soothe the mortified mother, who in turn insisted that all of this must be God's punishment. That the child, a product of sin, must be taken away and buried. Hannah wanted nothing more to do with the infant. She screamed at them to remove it from her sight and to be sure it wasn't placed anywhere near consecrated ground.

oOo

Jenny took it with her. Well wrapped and tucked under her arm like a small bundle of washing, she would do the necessaries. Dispose of it in a way she knew only too well. Jenny was as used to death as she was to the living, and with the extra coppers in her hands, she'd have no conscience about burying the tiny thing in some field or other. It worried her not. She wasn't one to judge people – and she could, quite easily, especially with some of the things she'd heard and seen. Instead, she went about her business, being midwife for the confined, and at the opposite end of life, laying out the dead.

Jenny enjoyed her work, especially the lively income that came her way when times were busy. And there were plenty like Hannah, birthing nigh on every nine months. It was regular alright. As regular as summer following a spring.

None would know from her that this day, Hannah Shaw had given birth to two. It wasn't Jenny's place to spread gossip and from what she'd heard from Hannah's lips, she knew it was best left well alone. The poor lass was suffering enough. A suffering that was to last a lifetime, she was sure.

19

It was a grey heavy day. Dull and damp. Not at all usual for the time of year. Hannah and Esther were busy examining cloth, trying to decide which would provide the best value on a shared basis. The hustle and bustle in the market hall didn't distract either of them from the task in hand, as the various sounds and smells attacked their senses. Both equally shrewd where money was concerned, they ignored the stallholders' obvious ploys to attract them to the more expensive fabrics and stood fast with the one they thought best.

'This one 'ere' the man insisted 'tis a much better quality.'

'Nay, this'll do us' Esther shook her head.

'You should take note. I know my business.' The stallholder began to unroll the bolt of calico that Esther had indicated.

'Aye, we know you do' Esther smiled wryly 'owt to get extra coppers off us.'

'I'm honest enough' he said sharply, scowling at them 'honest as the day is long.'

'We didn't say you weren't, but we know all about cloth,' Esther elbowed her sister in the ribs 'don't we?'

'Aye we do, and I'll wager we know more about it than thems that sells it' Hannah agreed.

'Nay' he said as he waited for them to indicate the length needed 'you can't know me, 'tis my business.'

'That'll do!' Esther cried sharply. 'Don't unroll no more. Rip it off there. By heck, you'll have us broke.'

'I'll not make much brass with what you buy' the man muttered, tearing the cloth.

'Aye. We'll not have much brass left with the price you charge' Hannah chucked. 'You'd think we were rolling in money.'

'My but you're a sharp one today,' he smiled falsely, glad to be rid of them. They never bought much. No matter how hard he tried he couldn't get them to spend more. They had to be his tightest customers.

'Hey – and stop him kicking at my legs!'

Both women turned to see Edward. Idly aiming his foot at one of the supports of the stall.

'Stop that right now, lad!' Hannah shouted. 'We're going home in a minute so just you behave yourself.'

'Jane, get hold of him,' Esther said to her daughter 'and go and find your brothers.'

'Where's my other two?' Hannah anxiously peered around her in all directions.

'With my lads, I should think. They won't be too far away,' Esther answered. 'I'll pay for this, then we'll find them.'

'I'll just go over to this other stall then.' Hannah wandered away from the tempting materials. Clutching shopping, and the young Sarah even tighter. She'd only gone a matter of feet when she spotted Hannah's sisters, idly wandering around. It was the limping gait of Lizzie that caused Hannah to recognize them at all. She hadn't set eyes on them in an age.

'Howdo, strangers,' Hannah greeted them with a warm smile, as if genuinely pleased to see them. 'My arms are full, else I'd shake hands.'

'Oh, tis our Harry's wife,' Lizzie said, in surprise.

'Eeeh so it is. We haven't seen you for a long time,' Sally grinned. 'Fancy seeing you here, of all places.'

'You've both grown some,' Hannah commented.

'Aye, we have,' Sally agreed. Looking with eyes going off at awkward angles, Hannah was surprised that the poor girl could see at all, feeling an instant pity for the child.

'You've had a new baby,' cooed Lizzie, moving in closer to the infant 'aw, it's lovely. 'Ere have a look, our Sal.'

'Aw, 'tis a she isn't it?' Sally grinned wide.

'Aye, she is,' Hannah said, proud of her infant. 'We have called her Sarah.'

'That makes us Aunties again.' Lizzie smiled, obviously

pleased at the thought. 'Aw, how nice.'

'How's your mother these days?' Hannah asked, out of politeness.

Both girls looked at each, then Lizzie's face turned serious as she said 'she's took to her bed. She's not well at all.'

'Oh dear,' Hannah sympathized. 'I hope she's up and about before too long.'

'Nay, it's not likely,' Lizzie shook her head 'won't last the year out, she won't. 'Tis her chest.'

'Is she that bad?' Hannah asked with concern.

'Aye,' Sally nodded, 'been badly for ages now. Has troubles just breathing.'

'I'll get Harry to go and see her,' Hannah offered.

'Nay. Mother won't like that,' Lizzie shook her head.

'Why ever not? He's her son.'

'That counts not at all,' Sally said. 'She won't want him.'

'I'll come and see her then,' Hannah insisted.

'Oh, you mustn't do that,' Lizzie looked to Sally for agreement 'she won't want that either.'

'I can't just do nothing,' Hannah turned slightly to find Esther at her back, and explained 'these are Harry's sisters.'

'Howdo,' Esther nodded, a light smile on her lips.

Both girls acknowledged the greeting, then hastily, so as not to be drawn into further conversation, bid farewell to Hannah and disappeared, as one, into the crowds of shoppers.

'Strange people,' Esther sighed.

''Tis a right rum do. Queer if you ask me,' Hannah said. 'Their mother's taken to her bed. They say she won't last the year, but she doesn't want Harry or me to visit with her.'

'You can't worry your head about it. Some folk is queer. If that's the way they want it, then it's best left alone,' Esther commented.

'Aye, but it doesn't seem right. If she's dying, you'd think she'd want to see him' Hannah said, perplexed.

'She were glad to get rid of him, and you were the fool,' Esther clucked. 'Come on, best find them childer of ours and make tracks. Otherwise, we'll miss that coach and I'm not walking all the way back to Middleton. And don't you worry your head about other folks' business.'

'I'll tell Harry though. He'll want to know.'

oOo

'I saw your Lizzie and Sally in the market up in Oldham this morning,' Hannah spoke. Harry, on all fours, careered lopsidedly around the floor, the weight of Edith and Edward on his back, pulling him to one side.

'Oh aye?' Harry red-faced, Edith almost choking him in her eagerness to hang on.

'You'll have no knees in them britches, carrying on like that,' Hannah admonished him. She had enough sewing to do, without him adding to it.

'I will,' he answered, loosening Edith's hold on his neck.

'They said your mother's taken to her bed' Hannah said seriously. Picking up young Harry who had been patiently awaiting his turn, she added 'c'mon Edward, you've had long enough now. Let Harry have a go before your father gets tired out.'

'Take Edith off too, she's damn near choked me' Harry breathed a sigh of relief as the older children climbed off his back.

'There's no need for swearing,' Hannah reproached, as she carefully placed Harry on his father.

'Hold on,' Harry commanded as he set off to circle the table. Young Harry began to chuckle with delight. Looking sure to topple to the floor, Edward, as young as he was, rushed forward to steady his brother.

'Give him one more round, Harry, then that's enough. He'll get too giddy otherwise and I don't want him being sick,' Hannah, her face full of concern.

'He'll be alright,' Harry assured her. 'You'll have him soft.'

'Will you be going to see your mother?'

'I shouldn't think so,' he answered, coming round the table for the second time.

'By all accounts, she's dying'

'I'll go to the funeral then.'

'Harry! She's your mother.' Hannah, aghast.

'Aye, tis the way she wants it.'

''Tis cruel.'

'She's a hard woman, Hannah.' Harry lifted the youngster off his back, then to the children said 'shall we give your mother a turn now?'

Clapping their hands and laughing they all shouted gleefully in agreement.

'C'mon mother,' Harry grinned devilishly 'your turn for a donkey ride.'

'Go away with you,' she laughed. 'I'm not getting on your back, I'm sure to break it.'

'C'mon,' he tried to persuade her.

'Nay, Harry,' she shook her head. 'Don't fuss me, I've no time for your foolishness.'

'Where's your humour, lass?' Harry rose from the floor, using the edge of the table to support him ''tis only a game.'

'I know, but I'm too old for silliness' she eyed him cautiously, ready for any change in his mood 'besides I've to feed the brid I a while.'

'I'll sit awhile and watch' Harry sat in his chair, then grinned roguishly at her obvious embarrassment at his suggestion.

'I don't want you staring like a gawp,' Hannah muttered, uncomfortable at his outspokenness. He wasn't usually around when feeding time came, but when he was, he took great pains to watch her intensely.

'I'll gawp all I want' he said, 'I'm your husband.'

'It's not natural for a man to be so interested in nursing'

she mumbled, lowering her eyes.

'In this house it is' he fumbled in his pocket for his pipe. A sure sign he was staying put.

'Please yourself then' she sighed, resigned.

'Aye, I will' he said, stretching his legs until both feet were balancing on the fender. Then yawning widely, he added 'and if you see them sisters of mine again by chance, tell them, I'll come when there's a funeral.'

Hannah tutted, showing her disapproval of his ways, and noting what seemed, to her, rather like a cruel smile on his lips.

Hannah turned into Kenyon Lane, having left the children with Alice. She'd decided, against all her inner argument, to go and visit her sick mother in law. Even Alice's words of wisdom hadn't deterred Hannah once her mind was made up. She felt it was something she had to do and ignored the thoughts of Harry's wrath, should he find out before she could tell him.

Shrugging off all misgivings, Hannah strode with a purpose, past a group of idlers. They, in turn, eyed her in the way they would, any woman passing by. She caught their comments but chose to disregard the idle banter.

Reaching the house, she tapped politely on the door and waited patiently as she heard sounds from within. Glancing towards the front window she detected a twitch of the curtain.

Presently the front door opened, but only enough for Hannah to be seen.

'Howdo Sally' Hannah smiled pleasantly 'I've come to visit your mother.'

The girl with crossed eyes seemed puzzled, then said a little nervously 'we told you not to come.'

'I had to, Sally' Hannah put her foot in the door to make sure it wasn't closed until she was good and ready ''tis only right that I should.'

'She won't like it' Sally said, holding the door tight against Hannah's foot. 'She's not going to be happy at seeing you. I'd best go and ask her before I let you in.'

'There's no need to close the door,' Hannah said softly 'I'll wait here while you ask. I won't come in until you tell me to. Go on then. Don't have me out here too long.'

Sally smiled then, slowly releasing her hold on the door, she disappeared inside. It was only minutes before the girl re-appeared. 'She says you can visit, but for five minutes only' Sally opened the door wide adding 'she's upstairs.'

Hannah crossed the threshold and immediately

detected a smell of sickness about the place. She shuddered involuntarily and chose not to notice the untidy and obvious dirty interior.

'I'll show you up' Sally offered, going to the stairs first.

Jane Shaw was lying in bed amidst what Hannah could best describe as filthy bedding, in a dank musty room. It wasn't something Hannah would be content with. But then again it wasn't her home. Each to his own, she supposed.

'Mother' Sally leaned over 'mother, tis Harry's wife.'

The woman stirred, turning her head until she had Hannah in her sights. Painfully, breathlessly she croaked 'you shouldn't have come. But now you're here, park your backside.'

Hannah looked around for a chair but there wasn't one. Not to offend the woman, she perched on the bed.

'Sal, help me up a bit' Jane groaned, 'then leave us be.'

The girl did as her mother asked, then eying the pair with suspicion, reluctantly went downstairs.

'I had to come, after what your girls told me' Hannah spoke then. 'It wouldn't be right if I didn't.'

'Ah, you shouldn't worry yourself about us, lass. We're not of your sort' Jane coughed, a loud hacking sound in the quiet of the room. 'Besides, you've enough troubles of your own.'

'Have you had a doctor?' Hannah asked, genuinely concerned.

'Can't afford them, lass, we get by without. Always had to. Always will.'

'I could help out' Hannah offered.

'Nay, I wouldn't hear of it' the woman took several sharp, shallow breaths, then continued painfully 'don't want no do-gooding ways of yours. I told Harry that. When he had a mind to wed you, and that's how it stays. I've nowt against you, mind.'

'What will your childer do if...' Hannah trailed off, unable to continue.

'If I die?' Jane finished it for her. 'Oh, they'll be alright.

Not much wits about them, but they won't come to no harm.'

'If they need help from Harry or me. They know where we'll be' Hannah said.

'I shouldn't think they will, lass. They're used to doing for themselves. Besides, you've enough troubles. You can come to my burial if you want, then after 'tis over, leave well alone.'

'We'll come' Hannah said positively ''tis only decent.'

'Please yourself, lass' Jane broke into another spasm of coughing, then lay back wearily as it passed off.

'Should Harry come and see you?' Hannah asked once she knew the woman would be capable of speaking again.

'Nay, it doesn't matter. Our Harry's best kept away from sickness and dying. Puts the fear in him, it does.'

'I know it' Hannah agreed, having also noticed that weakness in him. Silence reigned for a few moments, neither woman knowing what to say next. Hannah, uncomfortable, shifted slightly on the bed.

''Tis not for me to ask' Jane finally spoke 'tell me to mind my own business, but does our Harry treat you right?'

'Aye' Hannah answered, unconvincingly, her cheeks beginning to flame.

'Hah' Jane leaned forward a little ''tis in your face, lass. He doesn't. I can tell, knowing Harry of old.'

Hannah just started at the older woman. Unable to comment, unable to think clearly as the sick woman continued 'like his father he is. Sure enough. Too fond of the ale and the women, I know. Take note of a dying woman, lass. I knew all along he'd be bad for you. Same as it was for me. He shouldn't have wed you. You're too uppity for him.' She stopped, gasping for breath from the sheer exhaustion of talking.

'I think I'd best be going' Hannah rose, anxious now to leave 'and let you get some rest. I shouldn't have come.'

'Nay. You'll stay till I've said my piece' Jane seemed stronger of a sudden 'I'll have more rest than I need when

I'm under the sod. Come nearer, lass.'

Hannah reluctantly moved closer.

'Harry tell you his father died?'

'Aye, he did' Hannah nodded.

'An untruth. Not from Harry. It was me told a lie. Harry's a lot like his father, but God forbid he should turn out just the same.' She paused for a moment to catch the puzzled expression on the younger woman's face, then carried on 'he liked the ale, couldn't keep his hands to himself, around the young lasses, and buggered off whenever the fancy took him. Aye, he gave me hell, but I blessed the day when he never came back. You'll think I'm hard. But I'd suffered. My, how I suffered.'

'Why are you telling me this?' Hannah asked, not really wanting to know her past. Mrs. Shaw was touching too much on Harry, and Hannah didn't want it.

'So's you'll understand better. You were brought up different. More fancy with churchgoing ways. And I never figured you'd wed our Harry' Jane shook her head and continued 'couldn't understand it at all. You could've had better than him. Still, you took him, and more than likely you tried to change him. I'll wager it didn't work. I tried to change his father. Tried to alter his ways and in turn he made life hell for me. Do you know where he went?'

'You don't have to tell me all this' Hannah insisted, feeling more uncomfortable than she thought possible.

'Aye, I do' Jane assured her 'and you can listen. Mind you, keep it to yourself though.'

'I will, I promise you that' Hannah nodded, accepting that she must stay, at least for a while longer.

'Where was I up to? Oh yes, Harry's father. He buggered off good and proper. Said he was going off to be a sailor 'cos there weren't any work here. I ask you. A bloody sailor! Got sick if he saw water in a well. It were that war over the sea that caused it. Damn blessing it were to me. I ask you. Never done owt proper in all his life. Couldn't even make a good brid. All of 'em got something wrong. 'cept Harry of course. He's just his father all over again. Don't pity me, lass, I wouldn't want it. Just make sure you don't want for owt because of our Harry.'

'I manage well enough' Hannah reassured, hoping by now the woman had said all she intended to say.

'How many childer have you now?'

'Three of my own and one we took in' Hannah answered carefully 'and I had a miss.'

'Ah, all his wits in his britches I'll wager' smiled Jane, weakly, as crude thoughts sprung to mind.

Hannah blushed. To think this woman had an inkling into their very private side of life embarrassed her.

'I can see I'm right. Don't worry yourself about it, lass. Being a woman, I know all about such things. More so than you will.' She seemed tired now.

'I'd best make tracks' Hannah rose and made a move towards the bedroom door 'and leave you in peace. I realise now I shouldn't have bothered you.'

'Aye, I'm tired now. You've no need to come again.'

'I could do.'

'Nay be off with you. But mind out for yourself and those childer of yours. Harry's way is Harry's way, no matter what. Make your life for them – not for him.'

Hannah left the house thankfully, her mind turning over the sick woman's words. The more she thought about what was said the more she realised what Jane Shaw had been trying to say.

The woman was right in every respect. She knew Harry completely. And she knew what it could do to Hannah. Jane Shaw was older and wiser, having already had a similar ilk to contend with.

1884

It was hot and humid again. A sticky dampness, that made life less bearable than usual, clung to her.

The sweat dripped from Hannah as she scrubbed at the flagstone floor with grim determination and buckets of near boiling water. On all fours, her hands lobster red from the heat of the water, she pushed herself harder, her constant need for cleanliness driving her on. Meanwhile, the messages of weariness from her own body were completely ignored.

The children confined to bed, all burning up with raging fevers and Hannah due to give birth within weeks. She couldn't help but think back to the same time last year, when her dear sister, Esther had passed on. Young Jane followed a matter of days later.

The tears came easily to her eyes as sad thoughts sprung to her mind. Esther wasn't just a lost and dearly departed sister; she had been Hannah's closest friend. Grief stricken, Abe had taken the boys off in the direction of Yorkshire, and what he assumed would be a much healthier environment. She'd only one piece of news since, telling how he'd found farm work in some obscure sounding place in West Ridings. For the life of her, she couldn't remember the name now.

'It has to be done' Hannah muttered, dismissing the thoughts from her mind, and wiping her wet cheeks with her arms 'it must be clean. Can't have my childer dying from no fevers in this house.'

The very idea of losing any of her children through illness terrified her so much that her constant striving to make her environment as germ-free as possible became almost obsessional. She'd lime washed the bedroom walls several weeks earlier on hearing that some of her rather unsavoury neighbours had been plagued with bed bugs. Luckily she hadn't seen anything to suggest her home might be infested. She'd practically scalped the children when Edith came in from school one day, scratching in her hair with great vigour. Hannah sorted them out, spending hours laboriously searching their heads for lice. Cracking them with great pleasure, between her thumbnails, squeezing the life out of the little mites.

But the fever was a different matter. Having no distinctions, it crept in, unnoticed.

It made no difference whether you were clean or not. You either got it or you didn't. And those falling victim usually ended up in the burial ground.

Some said it was the hand of God, choosing the sinners. Yet others argued that the good Lord was taking those who'd toiled hard, for too long.

There were, of course, the know-alls, who blamed the fastidious for disturbing germs during too much cleaning; and those who blamed the unclean for the nauseating privies which gave off a most disagreeable stench in the height of summer.

Hannah had her own ideas, which surprisingly, had been mentioned by a few other people too. Water always lodged at the top end of Wood Street. Once it began to stagnate, the smell was awful. She'd even warned the children about playing anywhere near the slimy mess, sure it must be the source of all manner of sickness and disease. The rank odours pervaded her home. She'd been up there many a time and smelled it. Not that it was necessary when the wind blew in the right direction. She would keep all her windows closed in an attempt to lock out any chance of illness. Then making sure everything inside the house was spotlessly clean, all food adequately covered, checking regularly for furring, she would feel a little lighter of heart.

There were, of course, various concoctions to be bought from the corner shop, or the herbalist, to ease the suffering of the little ones. She would fall back on them if necessary. But too much medication was not something Hannah was particularly fond of. Though senna pods came in handy, now and again, when she thought anyone needed 'a good road through 'em'. She preferred to put her trust in good clean living, the better foods – when she could afford them – and an implicit belief in the Lord.

Alice had been popping in to help whenever she could, so easing some of the burdens. Hannah was thankful, in her time of need, though took offence at her sister's continual insinuations about the lack of Harry Shaw's presence. She knew that Alice was turning into a right old gossip and tried to dismiss anything that was said about Harry. But it was increasingly difficult at times. Hannah wished that Alice could find a husband, but knew it was nothing more than a wish. Alice wasn't interested, which was a shame, because it would obviously keep her a bit more occupied, leaving her less time for other folks' business.

Sighing heavily, content that the floor was as clean as possible, Hannah rose with difficulty from the flagstones. Flexing her legs and rubbing vigorously at her knees, she groaned, but with satisfaction at a job well done. Standing back, she admired her work for a moment only. Then pressing on, Hannah picked up the bucket of dirty water and slung the contents out the front door onto the pavement. She would get some fresh air now, then donkey stone the front – if her sapping energy lasted long enough.

22

They were sitting opposite each other across the front of the fire. Hannah was busy as usual, patching the children's clothing. Edward's pants were thinning at the seat and she couldn't bear to think he was showing his calico. The other children would only laugh at him, and Hannah wasn't having anyone laugh at her family, not for any reason.

Harry was watching her as she continued in utter silence, waiting for the words that would obviously come. He'd not long since come home from the alehouse. The chair creaked as he leaned forward for the pot of tea which was sitting in the hearth. With none too steady hands he lifted it to his mouth, spilling some of the hot liquid down his front.

Hannah clucked disapprovingly as his cursing reached her ears. Looking up from her needlework she gave him a reproachful glance.

Wiping at the front of his shirt with his sleeve he grinned at her and said, 'I'm not good enough for you, lass, am I?'

'Don't talk soft' a hint of a smile played at the corners of her mouth. He was handsome, she mused. Even now, not sober, and unable to control the simplest of tasks. She could understand why the women fell at his feet. The thought Annoyed her, but nevertheless, she managed a smile.

'What's going through that head then?' he asked, his eyes twinkling as he leaned forward towards her.

'Never you mind Harry Shaw' her smile widened.

''Ere, put that down,' he reached across to her and tugged at the sewing 'give your hands a rest and get your tea supped.'

Hannah gave up the cloth in her fingers. He took it and reached over, laying it on the table. She picked up her pot, leaned back in her chair, and clasping her hands around it, daintily sipped at the sweet soothing liquid, her eyes never leaving his face.

'The childer alright?' he asked without much concern.

'Aye, you might well ask, never seeing them' she answered.

'I work' he excused himself brusquely. Just two words.

'They won't be knowing you in a bit,' Hannah ventured, daring him.

'Ah, they do. They know their father,' he grinned broadly.

'You know me, don't you?'

'Aye,' she smiled easily 'only because I've seen you somewhere before.'

He light-heartedly took a swipe at the air, in her direction, saying 'you're getting a bit too cheeky, lass.'

'I speak the truth, Harry, and you know I do' her face turning quite serious.

Draining his tea, then spitting some of the dregs from his mouth into the fire, Harry put the pot back in the hearth, saying 'I'm an embarrassment to you.'

'Yes, Harry, sometimes you are' she agreed. For once he had said something she could readily agree with.

'Most of the time would be nearer the truth, lass' he raised his eyebrows quizzically.

Hannah stared blankly into the crackling fire; her mind busy trying to form the words that would not cause him to erupt in anger. She wanted him to know exactly how she felt about him in general. But voicing her thoughts usually led to the inevitable squabble, and his frustration ending in violence. In the earlier days of their marriage, she often caught herself trembling with fear on his return from the alehouses. Fear of the unknown.

But as the years went on, and the children came along, she found that she could successfully ignore him. Whether she would ever be able to handle him completely, she didn't know. Hannah did possess more intelligence than he could ever have, but she couldn't match his brute strength and his hold over her. His sitting here, talking to her, was one of the very few times in their life together that he even tried to appear the normal family man. It was something that didn't occur to regular.

'Why so quiet?' Harry asked, suddenly bringing her out of her own thoughts.

'I was thinking about you' Hannah answered casually, bending as she did to put her pot down on the hearth 'and how it would make a change to see you at Chapel with us, come Sunday,'

'Maybe, lass, maybe' he muttered, through teeth that held his pipe fast.

'Nay, Harry, don't say what you don't mean' she scowled at him.

''You're a good woman' he mused, blowing smoke across at her, avoiding the issue.

'That's the ale talking now, Harry, not you'. She waved her hands about in front of her, in a vain attempt to disperse the fog. Deep down she sensed he was probably feeling guilty about something. She could always tell, even though he was never openly forthcoming with her. She just read him too well.

'Nay lass, 'tis meant, you deserve better than me' he grinned.

'We can't change what is' she said, non-committal.

Harry watched her carefully as he sucked contentedly on his pipe. She was, he mused, not the same gill he'd ardently courted and consequently married. She was a much stronger person than he'd imagined her to be. But not in the way he'd wanted. She bore his children easy enough, was the central pillar in the household, and didn't let anything deter her great determination to keep the social standing she had achieved.

There was much in Hannah's favour. He admired her finer qualities. But he found he couldn't give her his all. The same as she couldn't give herself completely to him. He understood her but wasn't content to let things lie. He had to have everything his own way – had to have her yield to him in every sense. His male ego wouldn't have it any other way, wouldn't allow him to be that much less of a man.

In everyone else's eyes, Harry Shaw was everything a man could be – except to himself. To conquer the unconquered was his main driving force. And Hannah was still a challenge.

Sitting there now, thinking of how things could be so different between them, he felt the urge to take her off upstairs and lay her completely naked and defenceless before him. She affected him in such an animalistic way, that tenderness took second place in his desires for her. His prime need was to have her, without thought.

Watching her in the fading light he knew she'd be utterly appalled if she had even an inkling of what was on his mind. Filth she'd call it; not decent.

The closeness of their bodies, when lying together in the darkened bedroom, had her stiffening immediately any contact occurred. Harry hated it – found it frustrating – wanting only to love her in his totally uninhibited fashion. Just as he had done in the first weeks of their marriage. He could not understand what had changed her.

Instead, he found that which he craved with lasses much more pleased to offer themselves to him. It mattered not, to him, that most of them were usually full of ale at the time and hardly aware of their actions. They gave Harry what Hannah wouldn't.

He looked at her again, his desires rising more as he watched her – the cause of his own lustful thoughts.

''Tis you, I want, lass' his inner self screamed silently at her ''tis you. Nought else matters.'

He would come back home, forever at least until he broke her. Maybe if she knew it, he thought wryly, maybe she wouldn't have any hold on him anymore. Hannah didn't realise how easy it was to be rid of his lust.

The shadows danced eerily on the wall as the flickering firelight glow cast its reddish hue into every corner of the room.

'Shall we have some light?' Harry asked, breaking the silence surrounding them both.

'Nay - leave it be' Hannah answered 'I like it cosy like this' She preferred to sit in the darkening room. At least he couldn't see her too well then. And in the same way she couldn't see the warm smiles from him. They always tended to soften her heart, and he could be so personable at times.

'As you say' he agreed.

'There's been some talk' Hannah ventured carefully 'bout you, Harry.'

'Always talk about Harry Shaw' he replied, non-committal.

Hannah could sense him grinning in the gloom and knew it was his amusement at her discomfort.

'I don't like to hear it' she began to pick at her fingernails, to hide her nervousness at having broached such a delicate subject 'tis not decent.'

'Don't you worry your head lass, leave the gossips to me' he drawled.

'If you could just conduct yourself in a manner more fitting and not bring any more embarrassment home' she suggested, quietly, barely audible. She knew he could hear her. He moved in his chair and Hannah sensed his unease.

'What talk?' he asked abruptly as if it were of little consequence.

'Wouldn't be right if I were to repeat it. No decent woman could.'

'Come on, lass, out with it' a stern edge crept into his tone.

'By all accounts, there were two young girls scrapping at the mill over you' Hannah tried to control the tremor in her voice 'and I won't repeat what was said.'

'Who told you?'

'Our Alice of course.'

Harry laughed out loud.

'You shouldn't take all you hear as gospel. Especially if it comes from your Alice. They'll gossip over anyone at those sweatshops, lass. There's nowt else better to do.'

'There's no smoke without fire and I'm vexed about it' she said, adamantly. Angry now at him making light of it.

'Ah. Vexed, are you?' he taunted her. 'Then be all I want and you'll have no need of vexations.'

'I try Harry. I've tried, but you know I can't be all you want me to be. I've tried. I really have.' She began tugging at her apron, in an attempt to hide her embarrassment.

'You can Hannah – but your blessed Lord in heaven stops you. Be everything to me, lass. Be everything and Harry will give you no cause for palpitations. Ever.' He spoke fiercely, encouragement thrown in her direction. 'Be everything I want.'

She stared into the fire as an involuntary shiver crept the full length of her spine. Hannah didn't dare look at him, even as he leaned towards her; because knowing the man so well, it was obvious the way his mind was working now. Harry was deliberately being evasive when it came to his own character and make her, the main topic of conversation.

'Lost your tongue, lass?' he ventured

'Nay' she answered, eyes cast downwards.

'Well then?'

'Well, what?'

'You going to be everything I want?'

'You know I can't' she replied, sighing heavily, beginning to tire of his insistence.

'We'll have to keep on trying then' he laughed wickedly, reaching over to squeeze her knew 'a man is at liberty to see to it that his wife does all that he wants.'

'I've never refused you, Harry' she was looking him straight in the eye now, showing that the fears he once instilled in her didn't happen anymore 'and I've no intentions of ever doing so. A wife has a duty.'

'I don't want it to be a duty' his hand gently began to

rub at the inside of her thigh, his eyes watching her face intently. 'I want you to see it as a pleasure.'

Blushing profusely at his outspokenness, and deliberate caressing of her person, Hannah returned his gaze. She knew, without a doubt, the night had a long way to go. Neither of them would be sleeping until Harry's carnal desires were completely satisfied.

Hannah trembled at the thoughts, but seeing the glazed look in his eyes, she knew she would have no choice but to comply.

1886

'She's got a good steady hand on her' Alice said aloud as she watched Edith writing. 'Ere Beth, have a look. 'Tis good. Ah, you can tell which side she takes after.'

'Umm,' Beth muttered as she leaned over the table. Immediately she was crowded by Hannah and the children, all jostling to see.

'I can write too' Edward piped up, not wanting to be outdone by a girl, but knowing he courted trouble by speaking out of turn.

'We know you can' Hannah put her arm around him, hugging him close to her 'but Aunty Alice has never seen your writing.'

'Jealous soul, isn't he?' Alice laughed, her heaving bosom disturbing the two year old John who was dozing on her knee. Sarah eyed her Aunt quizzically, a little in awe of her overbearing presence.

'You shouldn't tease, Alice' Beth reprimanded.

'Ah, don't be soft,' Alice said 'I know he can read right well, I've heard him.'

'Well then,' Beth mumbled 'you'll be setting one against the other if you had your way.'

'It makes them learn quicker'

'Come on you pair,' Hannah interrupted 'this is the Lord's day. Let's not have any bickering.'

'Right then' Alice agreed 'get 'em all sat down and see what they can do. It keeps 'em from under everyone's feet.'

'Beth can sort them out while I make us a brew' Hannah patted Edward's head, smiling encouragingly, then saying to him 'go on, show them how I've learned you.'

It was only moments later, as Hannah set the steaming pots on the table, that Harry walked in the door. He scowled upon taking in the scene that met him.

'What's all this?' he enquired, shuffling over to the fire.

'We're writing' the children answered, with one accord.

'You've no need of learning that sort of stuff' he cleared

his throat, then spat heavily into the fire.

'Been in the alehouse again, Harry,' Alice said, accusingly 'when you should have been at the chapel with us.'

'None of your business' he growled, sitting himself down in his chair. Fumbling in his pocket, he extricated his pipe 'besides, I wouldn't want to be in your company by choice.'

'Humph!' she uttered, turning het attentions back to the children.

'Thought you'd have been home before now' Hannah said quietly as she handed him a pot of tea.

'I wouldn't have come now if I'd known these old hens were here' he smiled, and she caught a wink in his eye.

'You know they always stay on for some dinner after chapel.'

'They should be off home, not disturbing a man's peace' he was smiling at her, his eyes twinkling wickedly.

'You're in good humour' Hannah remarked 'what've you been up to?'

He didn't answer. They held each other's gaze for some minutes before Edith interrupted, climbing onto her father's knee, slate in hand.

'Look, loo' she said excitedly, thrusting the slate close to his face 'see what I wrote.'

Showing a little impatience, Harry nevertheless took time to appear to study the writing on the slate and mumbled 'very nice, lass, but learning's not natural. Not right for working folk.'

'Come on Edith, back to the table now' Hannah said hurriedly, knowing that Harry could upset the child with ease.

'You've not got young Harry and Edward at it, have you? 'Tis for cissies – soft folk – not the likes of us. 'Tis for them that has no strength to do a full hard day's work.'

'You're talking rubbish' Alice piped up 'we all have to learn.'

'Who asked you?' Harry scowled at her 'I've learnt all I need to know. There's no need for fancy learning in working folks' lives.'

'Ah' Alice continued 'you've learnt where the alehouses are, and other things I wouldn't care to mention in front of young ears. But that's as far as your learning goes.'

'Have you quite finished?' he asked angrily. Then muttered low to himself 'interfering bitch.'

'Aye, I've said my piece' she capitulated 'there's no arguing with you.'

'You shouldn't try then, should you. Because you know you can't win.'

oOo

'Here lass' Harry put the three shillings into her open palm, her sisters now gone 'a bit extra for you.'

'Where did it come from?' Hannah sked, closing her hand tightly around the money, lest he changed his mind.

'Don't ask' he grinned, then added 'if you must know I had a small wager.'

'I might have guessed' she sighed, slipping the shillings in her apron pocket 'but I wish you wouldn't.'

'I won. You should be pleased.'

'I don't like you doing it. Tis too easy a way to lose all your money. Winnings one thing, but you won't be winning all the time. What then?'

'Aw come on. Don't be vexed. Tis extra for you.'

'Alright then, I can do with the extra, but I'm not pleased.' She managed a smile. It wouldn't do to upset him. The man was feeling flushed and she must let him have his moment of glory. 'What was it this time? Something not lawful, I'd guess?'

'Pigeons' he answered lazily, sucking contentedly on his pipe 'I've kept some for myself.'

'I won't ask how much you've won, because it'll only get me vexed if you've kept back more than you've given me.'

'Aye lass, don't ask.'

'You're an impossible man, Harry, and God alone knows why I put up with you at all' she smiled as she ducked out of the way of his side swipe, then added 'I'd be careful who you're hitting.'

'Come here' he commanded lightly 'come sit yourself on this knee.'

'I don't think I should, Harry' she said, moving cautiously nearer to him 'I'll be heavy.'

'If I want my wife on my knee, then on my knee she'll sit. Now come' he encouraged her.

Doing as he bid, Hannah lowered herself somewhat tentatively to his waiting knee, then felt his arm grip her around the waist.

'There you are' he grinned, happiness brimming over 'you're not too heavy lass.'

'Aye but I am' she put an arm around his shoulder, more to steady herself than anything else 'I'm...I'm...'

'Spit it out Hannah, whatever's troubling you. Spit it out'

'We'll be having another mouth to feed before this year is done with' she said slowly, waiting for his reaction.

'Umm, what does that make it?' she felt his arm squeeze her middle.

'It'll be our sixth.'

'Umm,' he murmured, as if deep in thought, then added 'if that's the way of the Lord.'

'What with you and him up there' raising her eyes heavenward 'mucking me about.'

Harry had no answer to that. Couldn't think of anything to absolve himself of any blame she might place on his shoulders.

Patting her knee reassuringly with his free hand and looking her straight in the eye he said, 'not to worry lass, we shall manage.'

'I will' she emphasized 'I always do.'

'There's a good lass.'

'I have to be. And strong as an ox too.'

'You feeling alright?'

'Aye, champion' she answered, knowing that he knew she never had any ailments when carrying, and for the moment, Harry was genuinely concerned for her health.

Hannah moved then as if to vacate his knee, but Harry had different ideas and held her fast saying 'sit awhile longer, I want to ask you something.'

'Alright then. As long as I'm not too heavy.' She capitulated. Letting the arm about her waist pull her ever closer, until she could smell the ale on his breath.

'Will you learn me? Like you learn the childer?'

'What!' she exclaimed, almost unbelieving what he had said.

'To do my name' he smiled roguishly.

'You want me to learn you?' she emphasized. 'Me?'

'Aye, you're the only one knows I can't do it and I think it's about time I tried my hand.'

'After all that you said this afternoon. After the way you talked to our Alice', she said, incredulous.

'I couldn't let any of them know. Your Alice wouldn't have let up on me. She'd have been on her soapbox in the middle of Wood Street telling all and sundry' he explained, sure Hannah would understand him.

'Aye, I suppose she would, but that's our Alice. She can't stand you at the best of times.' Hannah smiled warmly, pleased that he'd asked her to help him. It had been difficult to keep it a secret through the years, especially as she had been taught both to read and write at an early age. Anything of interest in the Middleton Guardian, she'd read out to him, as she'd done with her father before. And now the children were learning, she'd tried to keep them away from Harry, knowing it vexed him when they rushed to show him their work for approval.

'You'll learn me then?' he asked.

'Aye, I will, but it weren't just me showing the childer. They learned some at school you know.'

'I know, but you showed 'em first.'

'Alright then. How many nights will you be here?'

'The nights I'm in' he grinned broadly 'we can make a start this very night.'

'What's the hurry of a sudden?' she asked, somewhat puzzled by his strange behaviour.

'Ah well,' he pondered a moment, then said 'if I can just learn my name, I can sign things that are important, instead of always having to do a cross.'

'Umm, how anyone can tell which cross belongs to who, I'll never know' Hannah mumbled to herself. Then as an extra thought, asked 'I could learn you some more counting. You'd know more about what money was then.'

'I can count right enough' he said arrogantly.

'Nay, not proper you can't' she disagreed lightly 'you only know what your ale and tobacco comes to. After that – well – 'tis anybody's guess. I should think like a lot of men you get robbed right, left and centre. Not an idea in your heads about the value of brass. All because you never learnt anything.'

'Umm,' he thought about what she'd said. It was true. All he knew the price of were his ale and tobacco. All else was beyond him. If Hannah wanted extra coppers, he'd give them to her, as long as he had the price of his pleasures in his pocket. At times it was painstaking, sitting out in the privy, counting out each day's coppers into separate piles, until there were seven of the same height. The remainder, not counted, went to Hannah. As truth would have it, he didn't know how much of his wages he gave to her. She just got what was left. He noticed the sour look on her face, many a time, but had never given it another thought.

'Aye, it sounds like sense to me' he said presently.

''Tis sense' she agreed 'and a bit of sense won't do you no harm. Maybe then you'll see the struggle I have making ends meet.'

'Ah you manage right enough' he humoured her.

'Nay. Tis only because I take in washing and baking. Tis

not what you give me.'

'I heard there's going to be a lot of changes when we get this 'ere town council, or whatever it is' he sucked heavily on his pipe.

'Aye, changes for the good of Middleton itself, but Hannah here' she pointed to herself 'will still be taking in washing and baking and having a hard time of it.'

'Maybe not. Maybe ...' he trailed off.

'Maybe what?' she looked at him, then carried on 'I can't see any sweeping changes coming our way. We've always had the commissioners before, and the council will only be doing the same. They've got a fancy name, that's all. And new-fangled ideas.'

'There's been a lot of talk' he muttered.

'Aye, well, we'll see, won't we?'

'Umm.'

'Right then' she roused herself 'shall we do some learning? You'll need it when these sweeping changes come about.'

24

The old man shuffled along, wheezing badly as he reached the top of the brow. Taking a moment only to pause for a rest, his eyes squinting in the stark sunlight, he mentally tried to count along the row of houses. The effort was too much for his tired brain and dismissing the idea, he turned into Higher Wood Street.

Sally had told him which house it would be, but not being any good at numbers, he knew he would have to knock at one or two, before finding the one he was looking for.

He found a kindly neighbour who pointed him in the direction of a half-open door further along the row, the while, standing on her threshold and watching him in a nosy attempt to find out his business.

He banged at the door and waited nigh on two minutes, until a woman, heavily pregnant, with a small child clutching at her skirts, appeared. She seemed ruffled, old before her time, but nevertheless managed a hint of a smile which warmed him through.

'I was in the back, pegging out' she said, eying the stranger with caution 'nearly didn't hear you.'

'Are you Hannah Shaw?' the old man asked, leaning tiredly against the door jamb; his walk up Wood Street had taken the wind out of him.

'I am' she answered, puzzling over his familiar features 'and who might be asking?'

'I'm Edward Shaw' he raised his cap 'Harry's father.'

'Oh my!' Hannah exclaimed, quickly covering her mouth with her hand in surprise. 'You'd best come in off the street. I thought for a minute then, that I knew your face, but I couldn't place it. Now I see. By gum, you're the spitting image of him. Come on in.'

She stood back in the doorway, pulling Mary to one side, allowing him to pass. She then followed him through to the back of the house.

'Set yourself down' Hannah smiled, eager to welcome him warmly 'and I'll do us a brew.'

'There's no need to put yourself out, lass' he croaked, his voice rough and cracked 'I'll not be stopping.'

'Oh, 'tis no trouble' she smiled again. Then turning to Mary, still holding her skirt tightly said 'ere Mary, this is your grandad. Say hello.'

'She looks shy, lass' he said 'don't be mithering the young lass. She'll be feared.'

'Nay, she's not so bad' Hannah ruffled the child's hair 'you're but a stranger, that's all.'

'Aye' he laughed then, a hoarse sound filling the room 'I'm a stranger to my own. They thought I'd been dad these past years. The best shock they've ever had, me turning up just like that. You weren't shocked though? Least not in the same way.'

'I knew you weren't dead' Hannah said, setting the pan on the fire to boil as he eased himself into a chair. Harry's mother told me years ago.'

'Now why would she do a thing like that?' he pondered, running his hand thoughtfully through his stubbled chin.

'She were dying' Hannah's face took on a compassionate air, 'and I suppose she wanted someone to know the truth, in case you ever turned up again.'

'Funny how she only told you' he looked up at her then. For an instant, she saw Harry. It was uncanny. Slightly unnerving. Hannah felt the urge to glance away, but his eyes held her fast.

'What is it, lass?'

'Nay, 'tis nothing' she mumbled, turning her attention to the pan of water 'but you are so like Harry. Two peas in a pod, from where I'm standing.'

'Hah, I'm an old man now. Harry'll look younger.'

'Oh aye, but you're the same even so.' She smiled, then added, an afterthought 'tell me. Why have you come back now, after all this time?'

'I wanted to see my childer once more.' He seemed sad

of a sudden, almost as if it were to be the last time altogether. 'Then I'll be off again. I'll not stop. I won't be troubling you lass.'

'Will you be waiting for Harry, then?' she asked, sitting herself down opposite him, heaving Mary onto her lap with some difficulty.

'Nay' he smiled, showing barely a tooth in his mouth 'I've seen him in the alehouse. Not that I spoke with him, mind. But I saw him.'

'Oh' Hannah muttered, a little perplexed, I thought you'd be wanting to speak with him.'

'Nay, I've seen him and that'll do. I'm not staying around these parts.'

'Not that it's any of my business, I know, but why not?' Hannah could understand the old man. Turning up like a bad penny, yet wanting to be off again, so sudden.

'Ah you can ask – and I'll tell you. There's no harm in telling you.'

She followed his eyes as he looked to the boiling pan and immediately rose to attend to it.

'I'll be going back to the sea.'

'Oh!' she exclaimed, totally confused. There was nothing about him to suggest he'd ever been a man of the sea.

'I've spent my life at sea, you know. Sailed the world I have. Seen things ordinary folk never see. Had a good life I have, on many a ship' he stopped abruptly, aware of an unbelieving expression on Hannah's face.

'You've been at sea then?' she asked, knowing instinctively the man was lying. She could read it in his voice and in his wizened face. For reasons known only to himself, he was spinning a yarn that he wanted her to believe.

'Aye,' he smiled as she handed him a pot of tea 'ever since I left home. Spent a good part of my life on the waves, and that's where I'm going back to.'

Hannah watched in silence as Edward Shaw sipped at

his brew. There was a kind of contentment about the man, but something niggled away at her as she looked at him. She couldn't fathom it. Without a doubt, she knew he was lying about the sea, and knew that he was much too old now, even if he was inclined to travel the oceans. There was a smell about him, not having been noticeable when he entered the room, but becoming more apparent as he warmed up near the fire. Try as she might, Hannah couldn't define it.

He glanced up and caught her watching him.

'Why do you look at me in that way?' he asked seriously.

'No reason. 'Tis the look of Harry about you.'

Draining his pot and setting it down on the hearth, he said 'I'd best be off now. I've a fair way to go.'

'You can stay a while longer. There's no rush' she offered.

'Nay' he wearily raised himself from the chair 'I've stayed long enough. Besides which, 've some explaining to do id Harry did show up.'

'There's no fears of that' she smiled knowingly. Harry wouldn't be home until long after dark.

'Just the same, I'll be going.'

'Will we see you again?' Hannah asked with concern, suddenly wishing the man could stay a while, or at least call again another time.

'Nay lass' he laid his hand on her arm, affectionately 'tis best if they think I'm dead.'

A cold shiver ran through her as he left the house. He'd made her feel strange about his visit – slightly unnerved even.

Hannah stood on the doorstep and watched him go, noting his faltering step. No sign of the rolling gait associated with sailors of longstanding. He appeared to be as exactly as he was. An old man. His life almost over.

When he was gone from sight, Hannah went back indoors, sniffing at the air as she did so. His smell still pervaded her nostrils, still hung around her. She sniffed again and shook her head quizzically, a little agitated as she still couldn't quite place the odour.

oOo

The following day, Sally, Harry's sister came banging and hammering on Hannah's door. Caring not for the commotion she caused. Just extremely upset and all a dither.

'What is it, lass?' Hannah asked with concern, showing the girl indoors. 'What on earth's got you in such a lather?'

'Has my father been here?' Sally spluttered breathlessly, having hurried. She shook her head negatively at Hannah's motioning her to sit down.

'Aye, he did. Only yesterday,' Hannah answered, worried by Sally's state.

'He never came back,' Sally said blankly.

'Ah, I see,' Hannah understood the girl's agitation. 'Sit yourself down a minute. Take a breath lass.'

Sally did as the older woman bid, then asked 'do you know where he's gone?'

'I don't, love' Hannah spoke sympathetically, knowing how confused the girl must be feeling at the strangeness of Edward Shaw 'but he did say he was going back to sea.'

Sally began to cry.

'There, there now' Hannah crooned 'why upset yourself so? He's been gone a long time, and not likely to have stayed. He said as much when he was here. Don't take on so.'

''Tisn't that,' Sally sniffled 'they've found a body in the canal up at Slattocks. It might be him.'

'Nay, lass' Hannah comforted the girl ''tisn't likely. There's bodies often found like that. Don't upset yourself.'

'Hannah' Sally, her eyes pleading asked 'will you come with me to have a look? Just to find out. There's only you and me knows what he looks like.'

Hannah sighed, her feelings a trifle mixed. The girl wouldn't be satisfied until she found out one way or another. And Hannah knew the ordeal of identifying a body, no matter whose it was, would be terribly harrowing in itself.

Presently she said to Sally ''Tisn't a good idea, lass. Are you sure about this?'

'Please, Hannah' Sally beseeched 'please.'

'Alright then. But I'm warning you, it'll be bad' Hannah placed an arm about the young girl's shoulders 'more upsetting than you think.'

'I don't mind. I have to know.'

oOo

It was Edward Shaw.

Hannah realised the meaning of the whole episode, when it came out that he was a pauper from the workhouse.

The smell of him, the one she couldn't define, was common to those from the workhouse. His general appearance should have made her see it sooner.

Nevertheless, both she and Sally kept their mouths shut and their thoughts to themselves. It wouldn't do to create a song and dance about the whole affair. It was best left well alone.

Hannah never told Harry.

''Tis best they think I'm dead' the old man had said. Edward Shaw had all but told Hannah of his intent. But she hadn't understood. Hadn't realised. Now she did.

Now he was dead – good and proper.

Alice was making her way home, through Market Place. She's been to a meeting at the New Jerusalem and afterwards spent a little more time at Hannah's than she'd meant to. Now it was late.

As she turned into the bottom of Townley Street she saw Harry, making his way towards her. Had she been a little quicker of mind she could have crossed over to the opposite side, thus avoiding him altogether. But it was too late for that. He was almost on top of her.

'Well, well' he guffawed drunkenly 'if it isn't our Alice then.'

The woman, hanging onto him fiercely, was the only thing stopping him from falling down in a stupor. She was giggling stupidly, a sight which amazed and annoyed Alice.

'I suppose you've just come out of the Railway' Alice said offhandedly, trying in vain to skirt round the pair.

'Ah and what of it?' Harry grinned, taking great delight in her efforts to pass him.

'Shift out of my way' Alice said angrily 'some folks have homes to go to.'

'Aw, you'll be wanting to go home then' Harry laughed. Then turning to the woman on his arm said, 'she wants to go home.'

The woman burst forth in peals of laughter, her brain fogged with the effects of the ale, causing instant mirth at such trivia.

'You'd best shift, Harry' Alice was becoming highly vexed 'and get her off the streets before anyone sees you.'

'Oh, telling me what to do are you?' Harry swayed a bit. The woman clung tighter. 'Well, it doesn't worry me at all.'

'I can see that. No shame in you is there?' Alice spluttered red faced 'And this thing, here' she motioned towards the woman in a derogatory fashion 'is as bad.'

'This thing happens to be Mary' Harry moved closer to Alice, his face only inches from hers.

'Humph' Alice grunted 'I'm really taken that it's even got a name. Now if you don't mind, shift out of my way.'

'What's the rush for?' Harry leered. Lurching against his companion 'got a chap waiting at home for you then?'

'Don't talk daft. I wouldn't want any chap after seeing the likes of you. Fair puts a woman off for life, it does. Now shift' Alice blurted out, putting her arm against him and pushing him to one side, a movement she thought would be easy, considering his present state of inebriation.

Not to be outdone by the overbearing female, Harry, with quick wit, caught hold of Alice's arm, just when she assumed she had passed him with ease. He held her fast.

'What do you think you're up to?' Alice, indignant, pulling against his grasp.

'Come with us,' harry laughed. 'The three of us can have a grand night.'

'Get off me this minute' Alice expostulated 'you're nought more than filth. Worse than an animal you are.'

'An animal, am I?' Harry laughed out loud, squeezing her arm tighter 'you'd be glad of this animal.'

'You want stringing up, and scrubbing out' Alice raged, as she finally succeeded in wresting herself from his grip, moving quickly out of his reach.

'And we all know what you need' Harry shouted as she hurriedly walked off 'a man. That's what you need. A man to show you what you're missing. You dried up old bitch.'

At a distance now, having heard all, Alice turned. Determined to have the last word, she bellowed without shame 'Hah! A man. Well, it wouldn't be you. You're as far from being a man as any woman could imagine.' With that, she turned on her heel rapidly, so as not to cause any further commotion, and went on her way.

Harry watched until she turned into Spring Vale, then became aware of Mary tugging at him.

'You shouldn't taunt her like that' Mary laughed as she pulled him into Old Hall Street 'she'll be telling your wife.'

'I don't pay no minds to her tantrums. I like to get her

all het up' Harry grinned wickedly. 'Hate the sight of that one.'

'Ah well' Mary said knowingly 'from what I can see, man or not, she'd welcome some attention from you.'

'Oh, I know' Harry laughed 'she tried me out a long time ago.'

'You're jesting' Mary stopped in her tracks 'you're talking soft.'

'Nay lass, I'm not' Harry assured her, a serious air about him now 'tis true and right enough. Thought I were too drunk to know the difference betwixt sisters.'

'You didn't take her on?' Mary asked cautiously, unbelieving.

'Too right' he answered, 'can't stand the woman.'

''Tis not like you to turn down a good offer.'

'I didn't want her' he said arrogantly.

'My God – hark at you!' she laughed.

'C'mon, let's be home' Harry said lightly, throwing an arm around Mary's shoulders and pulling her closer to him 'I've no need for that one. You give me all I want.'

'D'you suppose that's why she never married?'

'What are you on about?' he asked, steering Mary homewards.

'I just had a thought, that's all. She could have stayed as she is because it was you she really wanted,' Mary offered.

'Horse shit, Mary. Utter shit. I never in the whole of my life gave her any reason to believe I would ever want her. And I am usually pretty direct in that quarter.'

'Aye, I know' Mary agreed 'but it would be sad if it were the case.'

'Shut up, lass' Harry said firmly, but well-humoured 'forget the silly woman. She's had enough of my time for one night.

1890

26

Propping up the bar at the Forrester's in Old Hall Street, and sucking lazily on his pipe, Harry nodded absently as Billy, one of the regulars tried to engage him in conversation. Taking more notice of other activities around him than in the interminable chatter of the man, he attempted to convey his interest as he swallowed his ale.

Tapping his foot subconsciously, Harry's thoughts turned to Mary Murphy. A wide smile crossed his face. He would, in due course, make his way towards Little Park and a warm welcome she always had for him; but for the moment he was content to sup ale and ponder on the later hours.

Harry couldn't quite remember when he first set eyes on Mary. It could have been on been on Long Street where the young unattached used to while away the hours in search of a suitable partner. Then again it could have been outside one of Middleton's numerous alehouses. He fancied that the latter was most probably the scene of their first encounter, but as usual, he'd been a little the worse through drink at the time – fogging his memory.

From that moment on, their paths had seemed to cross all the time. He'd seen her with colleagues from the mill where she worked. And again, either inside of hanging around outside various licensed premises, where only the lower class of women would dare to venture. Harry guessed what she was, as talk in the ale houses always seemed to include Mary Murphy.

But he was content to bide his time and listen to idle gossip. She was, after all, he decided, the type of woman he wanted, and he wasn't going to let her slip away. She was everything Hannah wasn't, and he knew, without doubt, he would have her. Being a woman of loose morals mattered not. Harry intended to bring her to heel, brazen hussy that she was. Harry Shaw had decided.

It was one Saturday, several weeks later, when Harry,

tumbling in jovial mood out of the Pack Horse in Market Place, nearly knocked her off her feet.

'Ere do you mind?' her voice angry and indignant as she tried to retain her balance 'can't you watch where you're going?'

Harry caught hold of her to help steady her, then laughed and raised his flat cap upon realizing who she was.

'It's no laughing matter' she looked up at him. Green defiant eyes met glacial blue. And her anger faded as a feint hint of a smile played across her face. 'I've seen you before'

'Aye,' he slurred 'Harry Shaw to you my dear.'

'Umm I know' she smiled coyly 'and I'm Mary Murphy.'

'Well then' Harry slowly placed his cap back on his head 'I hope I didn't do you any permanent damage.'

'Nay, not at all. It'd take more than a collision' Mary laughed. Then added 'but I must be off now.'

'So soon?' he grinned drunkenly.

'Aye. Else folks will be gossiping' Mary was still laughing, looking down at his hand which still had a firm hold on her.

Harry followed her gaze, the guffawed loudly upon noting that he was, indeed, gripping her tightly.

Releasing her he said, 'we mustn't give anyone reason to talk.'

'That wouldn't do, would it' Mary spoke impishly 'nay, that wouldn't do at all.'

'I don't mind if they do' Harry doffed his cap, swaying slightly, 'see you around Mary Murphy.'

'Aye. Maybe' she said, turning to walk away from him. Then, a second thought he added 'maybe you just might at that.'

oOo

Within days they began to see each other regularly. Mary made sure that she was seen in and around the ale houses that Harry frequented until he couldn't avoid her any longer. They spent as much time in each other's company as was possible, not caring who saw them together. Ignoring any sniggering that went on, supposedly, behind their back.

In the evenings, without having to give any explanations to hannah, he would meet Mary, and together they would disappear into Alkrington woods, always returning to her house to enjoy a shared jug of ale. Harry enjoyed her company. Her wild carefree gaiety and the laughter they shared, brought him to life. It was all so far removed from the sombre surroundings that he had to endure at home with his family.

Mary seemed totally happy to be with him, revelling in his presence, enjoying his ale, and giving herself to him in complete abandon. Something Hannah was incapable of. Mary laughed with him, and at him, but never asked anything of him, content to accept what they had. While he was with her, Hannah never entered his thoughts. The two were totally separate and he existed as if divided. One half of each of him, running on parallel lines – but the whole of his mind with his green eyed wanton.

After four months of idyllic pleasure filled days and nights, Mary told him that she was with child.

'I'll be getting rid' Mary was adamant 'we can't have much fun with a little bastard in the way.'

'You sure 'tis mine?' Harry asked uncertainly, as Mary's past sprung to mind.

'Course 'tis yours!' Mary shouted angrily. 'I haven't had time to pee since you came along. 'Tis yours right enough – and I don't want it.'

'Hey, Mary' his voice became tender, caring 'now then.'

'I should think so too. How could you doubt me?' she gave him her widest smile 'I know who'll do it. It'll cost though. She has to be paid for her silence and God alone knows what would happen if this got out.'

Taking her in his arms, Harry held her close.

'It'll be fine, Harry, don't worry. I have done it before, and there's nothing to it really' Mary spoke brightly.

'You sure about this?' Harry didn't want the child, but at the same time, he felt somewhat concerned for her wellbeing.

'Don't worry' Mary reached up to kiss him. He grasped her tighter. Returning her kiss with ardour, then gently pulling away he said, 'alright then, lass, how much?'

'Half-a-sovereign' Mary knew the price by heart.

'I'll give you half of it'

'That's more than generous, Harry.'

'Nay lass, I should give you all of it.'

'Harry' she smiled at him 'I know you can't. Besides which, we both got into this mess, sharing seems right to me.'

'If you're sure?'

'Absolutely' Mary assured him 'now you leave it all to me, and don't mither about a thing. I don't know how soon it'll be done, so if you don't see me around, you'll know.'

'I won't come to see you then?' Harry asked.

'No, you mustn't. I wouldn't want that' Mary answered 'so we'll let things lie until I'm back to normal. Keep away Harry just in case there is talk.'

o0o

More than a month passed before Mary began to be seen out and about again. There had been much speculation amongst Harry's drinking friends, as to the reason for Mary's sudden absence from the usual haunts. Unknowingly some of them had hit on the truth.

In the Pack Horse, she avoided Harry like the plague. It wasn't until several days later when he got the chance to have any conversation with her.

Under closer scrutiny and without his usual belly full of ale Harry was indeed visibly shocked by the complete change in Mary's appearance. Pale and weak with dark circles under her lovely green eyes, she smiled at him. But the smile was cold and false. Her usual gaiety and impishness were non-existent. The sweet rounded figure that was the object of his desires was now a thin frame upon which her clothes hung, awkwardly. It was a pitiful spectacle that stood before him.

''Tis been quite some time, Mary' he said quietly, reaching out to grasp her hand, uncaring as to who might see.

'Aye,' she answered dully, pulling her hands well clear of his reach. 'Do you think that's wise, Harry?'

'Ah, to hell with them all' he said aggressively, as various people side stepped the two of them. 'Well?'

''Tis been taken care of' Mary assured him, her eyes completely lacking any of their sparkle, then added accusingly 'I hear you've not been without company? And up back alleys at that.'

Shuffling his feet, Harry stared stone faced at the ground.

'Someone by the name of Nellie – so I was told' Mary continued, then turning to walk away from him, added, an afterthought 'you're no different than the rest.'

'Mary!' Harry's voice was a strangled sound. Gas Street was not the ideal place for this conversation, but Harry didn't want her to walk away in this fashion.

'Nay, Harry lad' she hissed defiantly 'leave it be.'

Suddenly, catching her unawares, Harry made a grab at her. Dragging her by the arm, and pulling her very close to him, he whispered savagely through clenched teeth 'you can't do this to me lass.'

'Why not? I can do anything I want' she snarled, trying to wrench herself free of him 'you don't need me. You don't need anyone. Besides, you have unknowingly done me a favour.'

'What do you mean?' harry still held her fast, as he spat at passers-by, slowing their pace just enough to see who was arguing in broad daylight.

'My childbearing days are over. An infection they said. So, you see, Harry' her eyes blazed, her manner one of bitterness 'I can come and go as I please – just as you are inclined to do.'

'That's not fair lass' Harry released his grip 'it was your doing.'

'Aye, maybe it was, but I didn't expect you to have someone else the minute my back was turned. I thought we had something, Harry.'

'I'm no saint, Mary – and you know it' Harry smiled throwing his head high in the air. 'You know what I am.'

'Oh, I know what you are alright, and I'm telling you now. If you ever come near me again it'll be as business only' Mary told him vehemently 'otherwise, keep well away from me.'

'If that's the way you want it' Harry grinned broadly, amused by her fire 'then so be it.'

She turned on her heel, angry with him, and vexed with herself for having handled the situation badly. He was, after all, only a mere man, and she could well understand that he would take his needs off elsewhere, while she was lacking in person.

'Hey Mary!' he shouted after her. 'Let me know what price you're charging!'

Storming off at top speed, Mary heard him erupt into harsh cruel laughter. The sound still rang in her ears many hours later.

Mary Murphy with a well-rounded figure, green eyes, and natural fresh appearance had been born Manchester Way. Of Irish immigrant parents, her mother, a big country woman, died in her sleep without fuss having taken of a fever, leaving Paddy Murphy to manage his brood alone.

As each of his nine children, grew up, went into service, or found other means of employment, the man decided it was time to move on. Taking young Mary with him, Paddy, by sheer chance, found farming work on the borders of Middleton and Chadderton. He was more than pleased to be back working the land, as he had done in the country of his birth. The wages were almost nought, but they provided him with enough to keep body and soul together and to see to the needs of his youngest child.

Mary found work easy enough, and was, when Paddy had his accident, glad that she was with him to the end.

Being a man who enjoyed partaking of ale at the end of a hard day in the fields, he usually supped until his legs disappeared from under him. Often, he was found lying in a drunken stupor in some or other street.

He stumbled home one unfortunate evening, blood pouring from a gruesome gash to his forehead, incoherently mumbling about wild horses trampling him to the ground. The truth of the matter never did out, as five days later he passed away with an agonized cry of pain from his head.

Mary had then to adjust to a life of her own. Without the watchful eye of a parent under her roof, her comings and goings were accountable to no-one.

She, like Paddy, loved to visit the alehouses after a sweaty day in the mill and cared little for housework and such like. Thereby gaining herself a reputation as slattern and doxy. She didn't care much what gossip was afoot but enjoyed her freedom in a way that other lasses of her age couldn't.

The men swarmed. Young, old and married alike, were want to dance attendance on, and to bed, the sweet Mary Murphy.

At first, she gave them short shrift, but on reflection, realized there was money to be made from the drunken fools. Throwing away and the last shred of decency within her, she launched herself into earning extra from the pleasure of the flesh.

Mary found it hard to adjust to the fact that she actually enjoyed the lust of so many men, but eventually, she came to terms with it – accepting that she must be as wanton as they.

When first she clapped eyes on Harry Shaw, it was a strange combination of feelings that overtook her. Lust, carnal desire – yet coupled with warm comfortable feelings. Her men friends had never enticed such warmth from her. It was with awe that Mary knew she loved the man. Simple as that.

He had the most striking good looks, even when shabbily dressed, and he exuded a charisma that she found hard to ignore. At the time he was coarse and vulgar, a regular drunk caring not what other folk may say about him. She was drawn to him.

Mary didn't betray her inner feelings to him; she let him believe she was the hard-nosed bitch she was purported to be.

The first time he took her, it was rough and quick as she lifted her skirts up a back alley, amidst crude remarks from other drunks relieving themselves against the same wall. She ignored them, letting Harry have his way and taking immense pleasure from the touch and feel of him inside her.

This squalid interlude was to set the pattern to a life that was always to include Harry. Strange as he was, with his sudden changes of mood and humour, Mary knew she could only have of him what he would. With that she was content.

Harry was angry, and nary a drop had yet passed his lips. Kicking fiercely at the door and bellowing with rage, he kept at it, until with the sound of splintering the door gave way.

Neighbours came out into the street, but he worried himself not, hurling insults and obscenities in their direction, apparently taking pleasure in the fact that they'd come out to watch him. They'd seen such carryings on many a time, more so outside Mary Murphy's house, so all abuse fell on deaf ears.

Ignoring their jeers, he went into the dark house, slamming the door with such force, until broken from one of its hinges, it hung awkwardly, blocking the threshold.

Sitting in the chair nearest the glowing embers in the grate, Harry took out his pipe and with controlled anger, proceeded to wait until the harlot tuned up.

Darkness had fallen completely when he caught the sound of her footsteps outside. She was not alone.

'What the hell's been going on here?' her drink soaked voice floated to her ears.

'Leave it be' a male voice crooned as she tried unsuccessfully to manipulate the door back to its rightful position.

'Get off. Give me a minute then Mary's all yours' her voice was loud and insistent. Harry knew instinctively hat she was holding her companion's advances in check. That knowledge caused his anger to rise again.

It was mere moments before she saw Harry.

'Get him out of here' Harry hissed.

'Bugger off' she said to him, then turned to Albert.

'Come on, get your clothes off. We'll have to carry on. Pretend he's not here.' Mary brazenly began tugging at the man's jacket, in an attempt to wrest it from his shoulders.

'You could get rid of him for me' she whispered low into his ear.

Albert, very unsteady on his feet, with a courage fired by the ale, approached Harry. Laying a hand on his shoulder, he slurred 'The lady would like you to go.'

He didn't see anything when Harry's fist caught him square on the jaw. Soaked with ale, Albert fell loosely to the floor, then lay absolutely still, unable, through drink and a little feared of Harry Shaw, to do anything else.

'Bastard!' Mary screamed, dropping to her knees to attend to her prostate customer 'get the hell out of here before I bring the law.'

Harry, shaking with rage, and ready to do anything to appease his anger within himself, dragged her back to her feet, then hit out wildly with the flat of his hand. The sound bounced around the room and for moments silence reigned. Then Albert groaned, and retched, spilling the ale he had consumed in great gusts over the floor.

Mary cussed and screamed, kicking Harry about the shins. But he held her fast.

'You gave me crabs' she shook her roughly. 'Crabs do you hear me? You filthy whore.'

'Not me Harry. One of your other women,' she puckered her lips and slowly and deliberately spat in his face.

'It was you' he said drawing back his arm to hit her with the full force of his backhand. The blow threw her off balance and she landed in a heap atop Albert.

'I'd check some of your others first, Harry Shaw' Mary tried to lift herself from the floor, but with one foot, Harry pushed her down and held her there with his weight.

'Get off, you bastard' she yelled at him, writhing angrily.

'You'd best be a whole lot cleaner from now on, Mary Murphy, or you'll be seeing what I can do. And get rid of that excuse of a man.'

'Bugger off Harry. You don't smell so good yourself. No wonder you're crawling. A pox on you' she said breathlessly.

'Get him out of here' Harry spoke having ignored the

words she had fired at him 'if he spews much more, we'll be paddling in it. Can't take his ale at all.'

Stunned into silence. Not believing he hadn't struck at her again, she shook Albert warily.

'Come on love – time you were off home' she spoke softly to the man. While watching Harry for any sudden moves that might indicate another beating.

Albert moved then shuffled miserably along the floor on all fours towards the front door. Mary helped him find his feet as he lurched around, then guided him out as he staggered into the street.

'Poor man' she clucked, coming back into the house 'he doesn't know what day it is, and as to whether he's had a night of pleasure or not. Well, he'll never know.'

'He'd remember well enough when he found crabs' Harry said accusingly.

'It weren't me' she said in her own defence 'and you shouldn't even be here. I told you – business only.'

'Aye. 'Tis my business when you start spreading your filth all over the place.'

'I don't ask you to come here. What's vexing you – eh – Hannah caught them too?' Mary taunted him.

Catching her by the hair, he pulled her close to him, so close their lips almost met. Then he hissed 'she has, and it bothers me.'

'Leave me be' she twisted painfully but to no avail.

'From now on there's to be no more men' his eyes glared savagely into hers. 'There'll be me, do you understand? Only me. Your streetwalking days are over and finished with. And if I ever hear gossip, or catch you with another, you'll answer to me.'

'Don't you dare dictate to me, you bastard. I don't belong to you. I don't belong to anyone' she snarled.

'You're mine and I own you' he thundered, throwing her away from him.

In the gloom, she couldn't make out the expression on his face, but she sensed his mood was changing.

'I'll fix the door so it's decent while you get rid of the puke. Then we'll see about ridding you of the crabs.'

'Bugger off' Mary said, watching him cautiously as he went towards the party hung door 'you've got a sickness. In your head! Bloody sick you are, and since when did you learn how to get rid of the crabs?'

'Since Hannah showed me' he smiled devilishly.

'Alright then' she capitulated, anxious that he should stay calm 'you can stay this night without charge. But next time you pay – the same as everyone else does.'

'I've already said, you're mine now' he spoke firmly. 'I'm telling it's the way 'tis going to be. So, you'd best get it into that sweet little head of yours.'

oOo

Mary boiled water and together they filled the washing tub which they'd set in front of the fire.

'Get your scissors, lass. And make sure they are good and sharp' he ordered, helping her to undress 'thought you'd know about these things without having to be told.'

'I've had them many's the time' she commented lightly, dropping her clothing to the floor 'itch like buggery they do.'

'How did you get rid' he asked throatily, the sight of her nakedness causing him immense pleasure.

'Paraffin' she answered, winding her arm about his neck and grinding her hips, suggestively against him.

'This is a much better way' he held her close, running his hands down the curve of her spine 'more fun.'

'What did Hannah do?'

I'll show you' he said grinning broadly as he moved away from her and began removing his trousers.

Standing naked she leaned idly against the tub, waiting for his cure to manifest itself, totally unprepared for what was to follow.

As his clothing fell around his ankles, she stared open-mouthed in amazement at the sight that met her eyes.

'There lass – what do you think of this, then?' Harry's smile spread from ear to ear as he cockily thrust his manhood towards her. Erect and splendid as it was.

'Oh God, Harry' she shrieked, both hands rising to cover her mouth as the laughter bubbled within her.

'Well?' he was awaiting her verdict.

'Oh Harry, Harry...' she averted her eyes as the mirth burst from her in great gusts of laughter 'but...but...oh no...I can't...' she doubled in two, shaking hysterically as the tears rolled down her cheeks

'It looks like...oh Harry. It looks like a plucked chicken.'

'Mary!' he exclaimed, not as amused as she was.

'Oh but look at it' she pointed to his pelvic region 'you're ruddy pecker looks like a turkey's neck.'

'I'll have no more of this' he said firmly, shuffling towards her, his trousers still at his ankles, inducing further merriment from Mary 'you're going in that tub for a good scrub, then we'll have you looking liken a plucked bird too!'

'Alright, alright' Mary capitulated, giggling as she climbed into the hot water 'I give in.'

'I should think so too' he laughed. His fingers trailing lightly across her ample breasts 'then for the rest of the night we'll do what you and Albert were going to do.'

'All night?' she asked, expectantly.

'All night' he assured her.

1892

Beth and Alice strode as sure footed as they possibly could down the filthy street in Little Park. To constantly side-step horse droppings and dog dirt, took a lot of doing. Forced into the roadway at intervals in order to bypass the nauseating smells emanating from open doorways of the unkempt houses. Commenting in loud tones to each other they successfully steered they way around all the obstacles, aware there were eyes watching them. Occupants appeared on doorsteps and thresholds, watching the well dressed strangers with a mix of awe and contempt.

'It's awful here – ugh what an awful place' Alice crinkled her face in utter distaste, dabbing frantically at her nose with a clean lavender handkerchief while holding her skirts well clear of the pavings.

'They're disgusting. Really too uncaring' Beth shuddered, taking the shallowest of breaths possible, to control the heaving in her stomach.

'Ah, we're here. Alice said, moving towards one of the front doors. Without further ado, she knocked heavily with her balled fist.

They stood patiently waiting for an answer, the while running critical eyes over the whole frontage of the grubby house. Their faces mirrored the contempt they felt. When taking particular note of the none too clean windows and the front step that hadn't seen the colour of a donkey stone in months, they openly grimaced.

The door opened and the two sisters quickly switched their gaze upon the occupant, but not before she had noticed their close scrutiny of the outside.

'What's up? Not good enough for you?' Mary looked them up and down, her arms folded across her large chest as she brazenly stood on the threshold confronting her well-dressed visitors.

'We didn't come to discuss your lack of cleanliness' Alice's voice was filled with disgust 'as you rightly know.'

'I didn't ask you here' Mary tried to block the doorway as best she could, realising the two were women were desperately trying to see beyond her.

'No but we've come anyway' Alice said defiantly.

'You'd best state your business then' Mary matched Alice's defiance 'and be on your way, sharpish like.'

'You know what we're here for' Beth spoke. Suddenly she wanted to hurry and get away from the obnoxious odours of Little Park.

'Aye and I gather you know what we've got to say to you.' Alice dabbed at her nose again, fluttering the handkerchief to discourage the bluebottles that seemed to hover everywhere.

'That's a good one, 'specially as I don't know you' Mary laughed, her eyes twinkling wickedly.

'Our sister happens to be wed to Harry' Beth stated, her face a mask.

'Oh, I see' the woman in the doorway said 'she sent you.'

'Nay, she didn't send us at all. We've come without her knowing and we're telling you to leave Harry alone' Alice spoke aggressively.

'Hah, you should be telling him to leave me alone' Mary chuckled, beginning to find the whole episode quite amusing. 'I'll tell you what. Go home and leave me be. The likes of you shouldn't be around here.'

'You are a brazen woman' Alice continued, undeterred by the woman's tone 'and you're doing untold damage to our sister and her childer.' Beth nodded in agreement as Alice, to emphasise each word, jabbed her finger repeatedly at Mary Murphy.

'Bugger off, you silly pair of eejits. Bugger off back to where you've come from.' Mary leaned towards them, viciously, 'before I shove you all the way back.'

'Huh, there's no point trying to talk any sense into her' Beth directed towards Alice 'she's as bad as he is. And as for her language? Well – disgraceful for a woman.'

'Aye, I know what he sees in her and all' Alice glared at the woman 'she's from the gutter, same as him.'

'You'd best mind what you say' Mary warned, her whole attitude threatening 'if my Harry gets to hear about this, umm, there's no telling what he might do.'

'Your Harry!' Alice erupted indignantly 'my God woman, have you no shame? He isn't yours. He's a married man with childer.'

'He's more mine than hers' Mary hissed defiantly, suddenly hating the two hymn singing maiden aunts for interfering 'and that's how it'll stay. So go the bloody hell.'

'You'll have to deal with us, Mary Murphy, if you don't stop all this immediately' Alice shouted violently, her face purpling with rage.

'Oh yes,' Mary bellowed 'tray and stop me. I'll bed the man all I can. All day and every day if need be.'

Alice lunged forward then, and in the most unladylike manner, grabbed a hold of the front of Mary's blouse, tearing the material and shaking the woman roughly. Beth acted immediately and caught her sister by the shoulders, pulling frantically, as Mary fiercely tried to push Alice away from her.

'Alice don't. The gutter trash isn't worth it' Beth shouted as both women began kicking out at each other in wild affray 'stop it. Leave her be.'

'That's just a taste of what you'll get' Alice said breathlessly as she relinquished her hold on the woman 'so mark my words, you common ill-bred trollop.'

'Bugger off and don't you ever come near my door again' Mary screamed at them, the while trying to gather her torn blouse around her 'now bloody well clear off.'

'Oh, we're going alright' Alice gasped as she bent to retrieve her hat which had been knocked to the ground in the melee 'but I can soon come back again. You don't frighten me.'

'You're a stupid bugger' Mary said quickly, then slammed her own front door with such force that the whole row of houses seemed to shake.

'Come on Beth' Alice turned to her sister as she brushed the dust from her hat. 'Let's get out of this hole. Look at this lot' she indicated all the neighbours who were out on the street watching 'I'll wager it's the most life they've seen in ages.'

All the eyes of the street were on them as they carefully re-traced their steps back in the direction of Oldham Road, but neither Beth nor Alice paid any heed.

'Oh Alice, we've shown ourselves up this time' Beth said worriedly.

'Give over lass. She got what was coming to her, and if you hadn't stopped me, I could've shown her what us Adcocks are made of.'

'Do you think we did any good?' Beth asked, carefully scrutinising the pavement for any fouling.

'I doubt it' Alice clucked 'but at least all her neighbours know what she's up to now.'

'She didn't seem worried or fussed though.'

'Humph! Her types never are – they don't care for anyone else. It's our Hannah ai feel sorry for. There's plenty more lasses around, like Mary Murphy doing damage to other folks' lives. It's good decent ones like our Hannah that has to suffer. Harry Shaw isn't fit to live on God's earth, but he does, and it weren't dirty Mary, it'd be some other lass. Young Harry's living proof of that man's vile ways' Alice stopped then; all her anger having poured out in a torrent of words. 'Am glad that I never wed – never wanted to either.'

'Our Esther did alright though?' Beth volunteered gently.

'She's just one out of how many? Men, on the whole, are beasts. No better than dogs in the street. Vile, disgusting things who care only for their own comforts.'

'You haven't known any, how can you say that?'

'Well seeing the likes of Harry Shaw and his ways, I don't want to know any. He's enough to make any lass shy of getting wed. Believe me, Beth, I'm happy as I am' Alice spoke with a fierce conviction.

'When he finds out that we have been to see that woman, what then?'

'Don't worry your head about it lass. I've no fears where he's concerned, and I'll tell him that too. He's not fit to live in the same house as our Hannah.'

'Aye, but he does' Beth ventured.

'He does – when he's there.'

Harry, with his back to her, was ranting and raving. 'Oh God' she prayed silently 'take him away from me.'

Turning quickly, his arms now gesticulating wildly, he shouted 'will those nosy sisters of yours not stop? I'll be off and I'll tell them about their meddling.'

Hannah, heavily pregnant, sat motionless, trying not to meet his gaze.

'Do you hear me?' he bellowed, moving away from the fire and closer to her.

'I hear you alright. Half the street can hear you' she stared wide-eyed into his angry face. 'But I didn't send them.'

'You'd best tell them to keep out of my business' he snarled, spittle spraying, his face scarlet with anger 'my business is my own - not anything to do with them.'

'Whatever goes on that I don't know about, can't hurt me, but everyone knows about you and her. 'Tis not good Harry.' Her voice was calm and didn't betray the inner feelings 'it isn't fair on us. My, but you've not a care for anyone but yourself. How's it going to look when the childer see their father out on the streets with another woman on his arm. Tell me, Harry?' Hannah rubbed her hands over her increased girth, as the child tossed and turned inside her, frightened she was sure by the loud voice of the father it had yet to meet.

Harry glared at her, then clearing his throat noisily, he spat into the fire. Sitting in his chair he mumbled 'they've no rights knocking on folk's doors, poking their nose into other folk's business.'

'That's as maybe, but they'll be thinking of me' she sensed that the sudden burst of temper was ebbing away from him 'and besides, it doesn't look good.'

He looked at her, watching her face intensely, then switching his gaze stared at her bulging stomach. He thought he saw movements. Realising it was his child moving inside her, his smile spread slowly across his face.

'There won't be any childer from her' he said presently.

'What?' she asked, somewhat puzzled. Although she knew Harry of old, knew the way in which he would change and alter any conversation or argument, whenever the fancy took him.

'I won't be bringing any childer home from her – not like as happened with young Harry' he leaned towards her, his eyes laughing at some amusing ideas in his head.

'That's a blessing then' she looked at him quizzically, before adding 'and I'd prefer not to know anything about that woman. I know enough already.'

'You're vexed with me?'

'Aye. Too right I am' she answered angrily, having had more than enough of the man and his ways.

'Will you tell Beth and Alice?'

'Aye,' she sighed heavily 'as I don't reckon on you mending your ways.'

'We'll have no more said then' he dismissed any more words on the issue, by lighting his pipe.

Hannah knew instinctively that to utter another sound would bring his wrath down on her head. That was it. He'd had his say and he'd had his way again.

'Just look at yourself Hannah' Alice sauntered around the large washing filled table, her nose sniffing the air, as her eyes searched the room for any signs of dirt 'you even smell mucky – and can't you do your hair up proper?'

'Stop your moaning will you' Hannah said exasperated 'and say what's on your mind. I've more than enough to do without having to listen to you harping on.'

'I'm only saying what's true' Alice smiled warmly at the heavily pregnant older woman 'you do that much for others, you've no time for ought else. Just take a look at you – up to your armpits in the washing tub and none of it yours.

'Alice' Hannah stood up, glad of the opportunity to straighten her aching back, caused by what seemed like hours of bending over. 'You work in the mill. My work is here, at home, neither of us wears our Sunday best for those sorts of jobs.'

'Ah, but when do you get a chance to put your best clothes on?'

'You'd do better to give me a hand instead of moaning on and on' Hannah's voice became edgy.

Alice's face showed her complete distaste of the idea and she voiced her thoughts 'huh, I'm not touching other folk's mucky stuff.'

'It'd do you the world of good. Besides, it ain't mucky anymore. I've washed it. And as all the neighbourhood knows, what Hannah Shaw washes, is clean.'

Hannah dipped her hands into the tub withdrawing sheeting which she proceeded to wring and twist with great strength.

'C'mon, give us a hand with this.'

'Must I?'

'Well if you don't you may as well make tracks for home and be on your way – because I can't stop to pass the time of day with you.'

With a sigh Alice rolled up her sleeves and tentatively took hold of one end of the twisted sheet, noticing as she did so, that Hannah was smiling.

'You'll do anything for anybody' Alice returned the smile, glancing at Hannah's heavy stomach 'even in that state. You should be taking things a little more slowly.'

'There's no choice with a family to keep.'

'Why did you get wed?'

'None of your business' Hannah took the well-wrung sheeting from her sister and went towards the back door, saying knowingly 'but if you must know, you could say it had something to do with the folly of youth.'

Alice followed her out into the yard as Hannah pegged out on the line and persisted with the questions 'but why Harry?'

'He was a fine looking man.'

'He's not the best catch.'

'Maybe not' Hannah said, 'but he's a man, and to have a man around is all that matters.'

'He's never around.'

Hannah glared as Alice spoke – glared as if to say enough had been said, but the younger woman not content to leave words unsaid added

'Never around you any road.'

'What do you know? How do you think this brid got to be in here? Get back inside the house before anyone hears you.' Hannah rushed towards Alice, steering her indoors as quickly as she could 'and mind that silly tongue of yours.'

'Well - tis true.'

'Aye, maybe it is, but it doesn't give you the right to say and do the things you do. Like going to Little Park and dragging Beth along with you. By all accounts, you were almost scrapping. That's not the least bit ladylike.'

'She needed telling' Alice said defensively 'you are my sister after all and I won't have the whole of Middleton laughing at you because of him. She's from the gutter and the disgrace is so unfair. I could've knocked her head off her shoulders. I was mad.'

'I don't care anymore. It keeps him away from me...there! I've said it now.'

'What?' Alice stared open-mouthed 'How could you...'

'Because, dear silly Alice, if you'd wed you might understand. But as it is, you don't know the half of it' Hannah was a little flushed, but it was too late to take back what had been said.

'So, keep away from Little Park, and please stay out of Harry's business.'

'Hannah, he's been dallying with a trollop. How can you hold your head up?'

Alice sat down heavily in the nearest chair, stunned by her sister's attitude.

'Don't you care?'

'I could hold my head higher if you didn't go fighting like some alley cat. Come Sunday, and my head will be held higher than anyone else's in chapel. Because my childer are more important than Harry and his ways. Everyone will see.'

Vexed about the whole business Hannah scrubbed furiously at the washing.

'Does he still...' Alice stumbled over the words she wanted to say 'does he still...you know?'

'You're so naïve Alice. How on earth do you think this one got in here?' Hannah patted her moving stomach, blushing to the roots of her hair.

'Oh my God' Alice's hands flew to her rapidly heaving chest. 'How could you? In that condition too. He's an animal Hannah, a disgusting animal. How could you...oh my...'tis awful.'

'Alice, he's my husband and 'tis my duty' Hannah averted her eyes from the other's shocked gaze 'I don't have much choice in the matter.'

'You mean he forces you – and you with child at that?' Alice was visibly shocked by her own colourful thoughts.

'I think you've said too much now' Hannah piled wrung

washing onto the table 'and I'm saying nowt else. So, you can get up off your backside and peg some of this lot outside for me.'

'Well, I don't think I've finished my piece yet. 'Tis about time you showed Harry the door. What sort of life are you living? Him with his women, but it doesn't stop him coming to you – and drunk, more often than not. 'Tis about time you put your foot down. Preferably right across his neck.'

'Right Alice, that will do' Hannah shouted, suddenly very angry 'stop interfering. 'Tis none of your business. My life might not be the way you think it should be, but it's the way it is. And I'm not one to complain. There's many women have it much worse, so go and help them that need it and leave your nose out of my business.'

'You're too proud by half' Alice continued undeterred by Hannah's anger 'and I'm going to help all I can. You need it, so you'd best make up your mind to accept whatever comes your way.

'I won't do anything to his benefit, the animal that he is. So, give us that washing here, and the two of us will be through it in no time.'

'You've quite finished have you?' Hannah was still vexed.

'Aye, I have – and I won't say ought else, but it won't stop the way I think. Harry Shaw is going to hell one day whether you like it or not.'

32

Harry fell into the chair, dragging Mary down with him. Hopelessly drunk, hardly able to stand unaided, the pair staggered into the house, careering blindly against the walls and furniture.

'Eeeh but you're well gone' Mary slurred, her full relaxed weight holding him fast.

'Same as you' he smacked her rump playfully.

'Aye' she giggled, squirming in his lap 'we've had a right old skin full.'

'You know what'd go down well, just now?' he eyed her cheekily. 'A nice drop of malt.'

'Ooh, you've a cheek alright' Mary rose non too steadily from his knee, gripped the arm of the chair for support, and swayed recklessly over to the cupboard. Rummaging around amongst the crockery, her hands fell upon the bottle, kept as a rule for medicinal purposes only 'and mind you don't guzzle it all.'

'Just a drop, Mary, cross my heart' Harry laughed crossing his arms over his chest in childlike fashion. 'Here' she said, holding the bottle to his lips, in an effort to control the amount he swallowed.

'Aw, c'mon lass' he coaxed, wrapping has hands around hers, and trying to relieve her of the malt.

'Nay, Harry' she remained firm 'tis for emergencies only. If you go knocking this back, you'll have to buy me another – and I doubt you've got the brass to spare. Tell you what, I'll do us a brew and put a drop in. Then it goes back in the cupboard. I reckon you've had more than enough as it is.'

'Taking a man's pleasure off him' Harry imitated a spoilt child, winking devilishly as he did.

'Hah!' Mary mocked vexation. 'You never go short on your pleasures, from what I've seen. You have all you want and to hell with anyone else.'

'I'm happiest then' he smiled. A lopsided grin

spreading across his face 'when rutting like an animal with you, supping ale by the jugful, having a wager on the quiet and, of course, having the odd drop of malt on the quiet.'

'Ah, go on with you' Mary turned her attention to the hob, dismissing his ramblings, as she busily brewed the tea.

Harry watched her intensely. He had to strain his eyes to see her through the haze he imagined surrounding her. His head swam recklessly, his arms fell limp beside him as the volume of ale he'd supped began to take control.

Presently, handing him a steaming pot, to which she'd added barely the tiniest drop of malt, Mary said with concern 'Ere get this down you. It'll sober you up a bit. Then I should get some sleep if I were you. You're looking damned tired.'

Taking a sip of the hot liquid, Harry peered over the rim of the pot, eyeing her constantly as she settled herself down by his legs. Reaching out with his hand he casually ruffled her hair. Lingering as he traced the hairline with his fingers.

'Harry' Mary ventured 'tell me what you did as a child. You've never mentioned anything from your early days.'

'Nay lass,' he shook his head tiredly 'you don't want to know all that.'

'Ah, go on' she turned her head to see him better and smiled up at him. 'Go on, tell me about when you first went down the pit.'

'By gum, lass' Harry threw his head back, a chuckle escaping from him 'that's going back a bit. Hell. I can't even remember how old I was. Mind you, I don't know how old I am now, never mind then. Our Bill took me – up to Alkrington Colliery. I was nought but a child then and it seemed like I'd arrived in hell. Never knew what hell was. But that place came pretty close, to my mind.

'Hated it. Hated every bloody day and night spent below ground. It was hell alright and no place for childer. Grown men crawling on their bellies to put enough brass in their pockets, to buy food for the table. Youngsters like me were shoving trolleys – breaking our bloody backs. It was work though and nowt else mattered. We were feared – all of us – feared for our life. Still, we were thankful to come out with all our limbs at the end of our shifts. Which is more than can be said for some of the unfortunate buggers.'

'Did you have to go down the pit?' Mary asked, gently running her fingers against his inner thigh. Hoping, by her encouragement, to learn more about the man.

'Seemed natural enough then' he answered, non-committal.

'What about before? Before you had to work?'

'Ah I was a bugger then' he grinned as pleasanter memories came to the fore 'gave mother a bad time. You know we never had a bath. Didn't even own a tin one. Not that we needed one. Eeeh we had some fun. Me and our Bill, and sometimes little Albert, used to go for miles following streams and rivers to see where they went. Many's the time we fell in, clothes and all. I've had more baths in Wince Brook and Whit Brook than anything else.

'The Irk were worse. 'specially when we'd had a good fall of rain. Our Bill used to torment me something shocking. Frightened the life out of me at times. Threatening to throw me in when it were raging like mad. We used to take our things off and lay them out to dry the best we could. We've run, bare-arsed naked across fields and fields, clothes in hand, with farmers chasing us off.

'There was one niggly sod in particular, from up Chadderton Roughs. He were always running us off, so we got our own back by pinching a chicken. Chased it round and round we did, making a right racket. The bugger was clucking and putting up a damn good fight. So our Bill, calm as you please, wrung its bloody neck. Young Albert started wailing and spewed up. Mind you he was only young.

'We got the thing home in the end and mother was right pleased. Until Albert opened his mouth and told her what we'd done. She gave us all a bloody good hiding. But it were worth it. We had the best dinner we'd had in ages. By gum, we didn't half get into some scrapes.'

Draining her pot, Mary reached towards the hearth, setting it there.

Harry followed suit. His hands free, Mary boldly sat astride his knee and snuggled close, feeling his strong arms wrap around her. In the warmth and comfort of his nearness, her eyelids began to grow heavy as sleep threatened to wash over her.

But she strived against all odds to stay alert upon realising that Harry was unexpectedly talking again. Mary knew it was the ale as soon as his words reached her ears. Of a sudden he was rambling along and, although it disturbed her, she was determined not to miss anything.

From her past experience with male callers she knew that, in most cases, they undoubtedly regretted all said when sobriety returned. Usually, Harry said nothing. Mary, as a rule, closed her ears to any confessions of the soul. But with Harry, she ached to learn more of the man. She was hungry to know all there was and praised the good fortune that was instrumental in loosening his normally well-guarded tongue.

'Ah you should have seen her, the first time I did' Harry sighed contentedly, his eyes fixed steadily on the flames, dancing haphazardly in the grate. 'Bloody lovely she was. Clean and sweet as new. I'd just come out of the pit, full of muck and filth. Sweat and coal dust caked on hard – black as the hobs of hell. I was tired. Dead on my feet. Every bone aching for my bed. Ah, she was a sight alright, brightening me up no end. She looked so decent and from right gradely folk and all. I had to have her.

'I decided there and then to have her for my own. Never had ought of my own – not ever. All my clothes were handed down. I couldn't ever have anything for myself – had to share all the time. Till I got her. Then I had something that belonged only to me. And what a damned good feeling that were.

'I can't stand the churchgoing. Too much of it for my liking. Full of fancy ways they are, the lot of them.' Harry continued as if totally ignorant of Mary's being there 'have their own pew now and go to all church meetings. Bores the arse off me. I never went, not being from god fearing folk. My mother had enough to raising us. She sure as hell didn't have time to take on fancy ways.

'I was brought up rough. She was more on the gentle side. She knew about learning. Has all the childer learned too, just like high class folk do – with proper ways and all.

'She'd like to learn me some fancy ways but I'll have none of it. I'm working class and that's as it stays' an edge of bitterness creeping into his voice.

'Harry' Mary interrupted with concern, noting the change in him 'I think we should be off upstairs – you are staying?'

'Aye' he sighed, squeezing her tightly 'I'm staying alright. There's not much for me at home. Besides, why should I go home when all I need is here in the comfort of your hovel?'

'Harry Shaw!' she exclaimed, sitting bolt upright 'tis nay so bad.'

'Oh, but it is' he grinned, pulling her back to him. 'I'm not complaining mind. I like it this way. If it suits you and it suits me then everyone else can go to hell.'

'Oh Harry' she murmured close against his ear 'whatever would I do without you?'

'Have no worries lass – you won't ever have to do without me.'

'I think there'll be a wedding, soon' Edith commented, eager that her father should know. Not that he knew much of what went on anyway, but this was important as far as Edith was concerned.

'I'd be a happy man to be shut of you' Harry said, a snide smile on his face who's the unlucky chap?'

'Not me, father' Edith insisted 'our Edwards.'

'More's the pity' Harry grunted, his attention returning to the cleaning of his pipe.

'We don't know for sure, Edith' Hannah shook her head, hoping to steer her daughter away from the subject.

'Ah, but I've seen him and Agnes and I don't think they'll be waiting too long.' Edith continued, refusing to let her notions pass by 'can't keep away from each other, they can't.'

'Jealous, are you?' Harry turned to her then 'jealous because no-one in his right mind would have you?'

'That's unfair Harry' hannah jumped in 'Edith hasn't met anyone yet.'

'And never likely to either.'

'Ah, she will' Hannah insisted, then turning to Edith, said 'won't you?'

'When I've got a mind to, but I'll not wed just to please anyone' Edith glanced in the direction of her father, showing that by 'anyone' she meant him in particular.

Harry grunted, then scowled at her. He'd caught her meaning right enough.

'She's a nice lass and from a good family, so I've heard, 'Hannah said lightly, hoping to steer Harry and Edith away from a possible argument.

'Aye' Edith agreed 'some of her relations have a shop down Old Road.'

They both turned automatically as they heard the click of the latch to see Edward appear in the doorway.

''Bout time too' Hannah clucked, rising sharply to

attend to the lad's tea 'we've been waiting on you.'

'I was talking' Edward beamed, shoving his cap into his jacket pocket, then hanging the coat up.

'Courting I'll wager' Edith grinned knowingly, as she laid the plate on the table 'ere, sit yourself down and eat up, you must be clemmed.'

'Talking I said' Edward insisted 'and talking was all.'

'Must have been interesting, to keep you from your tea' Hannah commented 'there's only one thing I know, keeps a healthy appetite from the table.'

'Take no heed, lad' Harry entered into the general banter 'they've been gassing again. Near got you wed they have.'

'Umm' Edward mumbled, his mouth full.

'Have none of it, lad' Harry offered his opinion 'keep well away from women; nowt but trouble they are.'

'Ah well you'll know all about that sort of thing,' Hannah could have bitten off her own tongue as soon as the words slipped out, as she watched Harry's face with extreme caution.

'Aye, I would' harry scowled 'I've had enough around me.'

Hannah breathed easily then. A tense moment had passed. She caught Edith eyeing her warily, busily cleaning the table.

'Can I bring Agnes home?' Edward asked, cautiously.

'What do you say, father?' Hannah directed his words towards Harry 'shall Edward bring his lass to show us?'

'Aye, he'd best do' Harry shifted in his chair 'but I'm not dressing up; not even for fancy folk.'

Edith raised her eyes to the ceiling in frustration, silently mouthing in Edward's direction 'he's impossible.'

Edward quietly nodded in agreement.

Harry looked up then, having just missed what went on. 'Will that do lad?'

'Aye' Edward beamed.

'Good' Hannah smiled 'that's settled then. Bring her

round to tea, come Sunday.'

Edward grinned.

'You'll be in' Hannah asked Harry.

'I shall have to be, won't I' he answered, the whole business bringing to mind his own courtship of Hannah, and how difficult Frank Adcock had been.

'And mind you're not the worse for drink' Hannah added knowingly.

'I'll be as I want to be in my own home' Harry said, his manner completely arrogant. 'That'll put fear in the lass' Hannah eyed him with contempt, sick and tired of the weary years of his endless ways.

'I'm not that bad' he smiled roguishly.

'Umm. Well, that's your opinion' she grunted to herself, then in much stronger tones 'I want your best behaviour, no matter what.'

'You won't need to be too fussed, mother' Edward said lightly. Then stretching, his arms raised into the air, said 'I'll be off out for a couple of hours.'

'Going to see your lady love?' Edith teased.

'Mind your own business' he answered, assuming an air of importance.

'Well if you're going out' Hannah said 'and you happen to see John on your travels, send him home, sharpish like. 'Tis getting on and time he were indoors.'

'He was idling down by the horse trough last I saw of him' Edward volunteered.

'Ah well, he'll more than likely still be there' Hannah said knowingly 'so tell him to get a gait on. And don't forget to let Agnes know she's invited.

34

Edward married Agnes. It was a grand do, they said. Agnes looking every inch the radiant bride in a beautiful dress that she and her mother had spent hours sewing to perfection. Edward, equally smart in a suit he'd splashed out on for the special occasion stood awaiting Agnes, side by side with young Harry, his best man. There was the usual fumbling for the ring, accompanied by tense silence from the pews as the younger brother delved into his pockets. Followed by the collective sigh of relief when it was proffered to the minister in the, near full, Salem Chapel.

Hannah, proud of her lads, allowed a smile to form on her lips as she watched the procedure. Harry, looking clean and well dressed for once, sat equally proud by her side. Hannah was well pleased, happier than she had been in a long time. All her family were present, including her own brother James and his wife, who'd travelled all the way from Scarborough, especially for the wedding.

Harry, the while, was visualising the ale to come when the wedding party took themselves over to the Dusty Miller. Then it would be a grand do, alright. Weddings weren't something special otherwise. Edith sitting by her mother, had Elizabeth squirming uncomfortably on her knee. The child was more than anxious to be off and would have preferred, as youngsters are inclined, to be crawling around the floor and generally causing mischief. It was only Edith's firm hand and the reproachful glances from Hannah, that kept the child in check.

The ceremony over, with Edward and Agnes now Mr. and Mrs. Shaw, the children were relieved from being on their best behaviour, and the adults full of joy and congratulations. The photographs were taken by the Jackson brothers, Agnes' parents insisting on engaging their services as only the best was good enough for their daughter – and be blowed with the cost. The decision was impressive, causing sighs of wonder and amazement from friends and neighbours, anxious to squeeze onto photographs. Many having never had such a chance before, and at no cost to themselves. It was an opportunity not to be missed, during the general excitement and hubbub of the day.

The Dusty Miller, for the reception, proved to be right up Harry's street, and the same to Agnes' parents. Hannah, a trifle vexed by the sight of Edward's new in-laws staggering around in double quick time, tried not to show it, making allowances for the gaiety and exuberant mood of the gathered families. But nevertheless, she watched them intensely, hoping against hope, they weren't want to drink themselves senseless on a regular basis. The thought appalled her. One drunk in the family was more than enough.

The end of the evening came none too soon for Hannah. As Edward and Agnes said their goodbyes, she joined in wholeheartedly, not wanting to appear totally out of it. Not only had Harry made a sorry spectacle of himself, so had others. And it displeased her.

The happy couple, amongst much laughter, singing and kissing, took their leave up to John Street, and their very first home.

Hannah, as soon as was decently possible, collected her brood about her, and together they made their excuses, amidst much hand shaking and more congratulations. As a group, cheerful and tired, the children now extremely fractious at such a late hour, they made their way home.

Harry didn't join them. He was staying a while longer, determined to make the most of the chance to swill ale.

1894

Seething with blind rage, Harry mounted the stairs, two at a time. Crashing violently into the bedroom, he lunged at one of the shadowy figures lying in the bed and tore at the blankets and sheets until she was uncovered.

Cowering with fright, Sarah, dazed by sleep, tried unsuccessfully to back away from his reaching grasp.

'With child eh? Filth! Whore!' harry bellowed, dragging her from the bed and the room in one fierce movement, leaving Mary and Ann, bot shaking from head to toe at their abrupt awakening.

'Oh please father, please father don't' the terrified girls begged as Harry pulled her roughly downstairs, then threw her bodily into the kitchen.

Falling heavily against the sofa, Sarah hung there, too feared to even look at him as he cursed and raved like some madman.

Leave her be' hannah spoke calmly, moving towards the sobbing girl and wishing she hadn't mentioned her daughter's condition at all 'there's no need of this carry on.'

'Whore!' he bellowed, cracking Sarah sharply about the head, completely ignoring the presence of his wife and elder daughter. 'I should bloody well horse whip you for this.'

'Leave her!' Hannah cried out, becoming frightened by his temper. Yet instinctively putting herself between them to offer Sarah some protection.

Harry, determined to appease his anger, shoved his wife to one side and let fly with his powerful hands. Hands which rained blows on Sarah without pity, until she cried out in her pain and suffering.

It was Edith, who with quick wit and highly vexed by the spectacle, reached for the poker resting in the hot fire, ready to make him stop at all costs.

Brandishing the glowing iron, Edith waved it as close to her father as she dared, saying angrily 'you'd best give over.'

He looked to Edith, poker at the ready, and realised at that moment exactly what she was capable of. It had the desired effect. Reluctantly moving away from the sobbing Sarah, who was now being comforted by her mother, he skirted Edith with caution.

'She'll get more of the same if she doesn't shut up' Harry shouted, eyes still on Edith, ready to also give her the biggest hiding of her life, if and when she released the poker.

''Tis your doing' Hannah spat angrily.

'My doing! Mt doing!' he ranted. 'I didn't get her into that state. Dirty filthy whore, she is, bringing shame into this house. She is no daughter of mine.'

Hannah, open-mouthed in astonishment, couldn't find the words. He was unbelievable. To punish the girl so severely, when it was he, himself, who had brought more shame home than any of his children could – it was totally beyond reason.

'Who did it?' he demanded, fists clenched, lips tight set.

'Don't tell him' Edith said of a sudden, urging her sister to keep silent on the matter.

'Hold your tongue, lass, this is not your business' he barked at her, then directing his voice at Sarah 'I asked you - who got you into this state?'

Sarah, sobbing violently against her mother's breast, didn't answer.

'Can't you see' Hannah looked up at him. 'The lass is too upset to tell you anything.'

'By God' he thundered, knocking Edith off balance in an attempt to grab a hold of Sarah 'you'll tell me or you're out of this house!'

'No, harry. Leave it be. Let it lie till morning' Hannah implored, knowing without a doubt that Harry would have his way.

'Tell me!' he snarled, dragging Sarah from the safety of her mother's arms 'tell me and I'll have the bugger's guts.'

'Mother' Sarah whimpered, his grasp tightening.

'Don't look to her' Harry roughly steered Sarah towards the back door 'she can't help you now.'

'Harry' Hannah's eyes met his and for a moment they held each other's gaze. He knew she was begging him not to do it. He knew. But it mattered not. He must finish what he started. He mustn't hesitate, mustn't bend to them. He had to make them see that he was only doing what any decent father would do.

'She's getting out of this house and I don't want to ever see her under this roof again' he yanked the door open and without further ado, pushed her out into the yard. Then slamming the door shut he bellowed 'and you can get out of the yard. Get on the street where you belong!'

Hannah stared at the floor in an attempt to stem the tears forming in her eyes. Her heart ached, the pain almost too much to bear. The thoughts of Sarah flung into the night. He'd hurt her more than he could ever know. Tore a loved one from her. But she wouldn't weep, not in front of him. He wasn't going to have everything his own way.

Harry sat in his chair now, gripping the arms fiercely, as the rage burned within him.

'I shall go after her' Edith decided, dropping the poker in the hearth with a deafening clang. Not having the nerve to use it in anyone's defence she felt silly now. Her surge of courage having vanished in an instant.

'You'll stay put!' Harry growled. 'Go out that door and you'll bloody well stay out there too.'

Hannah trembled as she watched Edith walk, with a strange defiance, towards the door.

'Useless bitch' Harry yelled 'go on, get out, bugger off. We're well shut of the lot of you.'

'I shall find her, mother' Edith smiled reassuringly, completely ignoring her father and his insults. 'Fret none, I'll be with her.'

'They need never come back' Harry said, undoing his clogs and kicking them to one side as the door closed behind his elder daughter. 'I won't have them under this roof again.'

Hannah didn't answer. He wasn't worth the breath.

Instead, silence descended. Angry and menacing, threatening to erupt again at the slightest provocation.

The Nowster began to ring. Harry grunted.

Hannah worried. For her, it would be a long night.

oOo

It was early morning, the light still cold and grey, as Hannah stood by the horse trough, waiting for Edward.

Having lain awake most of the night with worries and possible solutions, Hannah decided it was best to have words with her eldest. He'd know what to do. He'd know how to handle his father better than she could.

Once Harry left for work, she'd given him enough time to be well out of the way. Then hurriedly dashing off down Wood Street, she hoped to catch Edward before he took his first lot of passengers to Manchester.

Through the gloom, Hannah caught sight of him, busying himself with the wagonette. She shouted unashamedly to draw his attention.

'Mother' he called back, immediately coming towards her 'what brings you here at this hour?'

'Oh Edward, Edward' she stumbled towards him 'thank the Lord I've managed to catch you.'

'What's wrong, mother?' Edward asked concernedly, noting how pale and troubled she seemed.

''Tis your father' Hannah babbled out breathlessly 'he threw our Sarah out, last night. And Edith too.'

'Oh God' he mumbled, anger welling up within him 'what on earth did he do that for?'

Hannah told him. She told him everything. Then she waited for what seemed like an age for his reaction.

Presently, he said 'what do you want me to do?'

'You might speak to your father' she said hesitantly.

'Mother' he took hold of her arm 'he only did what he

thought was right. I'd most probably have done exactly the same as he has. So really, it isn't for me to interfere.'

'Oh Edward' she mumbled, disappointed, not knowing now which way to turn. She had expected a little more compassion from her eldest.

'Listen' he turned her to face him 'you'd do best to find out who the chap is. Who's the cause. He's going to have to wed our Sarah, no matter what. And I'll make sure he does.'

'She won't tell us' Hannah looked to him for the support she needed.

'She will' he said knowingly. 'Anyway, I have to go ow but I promise I'll have words with father, later on. I don't see what I can do, him being right for once. But I'll see.'

'If you can get him to calm down a bit and see some sense, we can help her then. But how can I do anything when he's not prepared to let her come home?'

'She's shamed him, mother. He'll be hurt by it' Edward said.

'He shamed himself years ago.'

'That's as maybe, but it has nought to do with what she's done.'

'He's done much worse' Hannah mumbled quietly, totally disappointed with Edward's attitude.

'I won't argue with you, mother, I don't have the time' Edward leaned forward and kissed her on the cheek. 'Now be off home and go about your business. All will come right in the end.'

She smiled at him then. The way she was feeling, her smile was difficult – but she made the effort.

'Go, be off' he grinned as he turned towards his wagonette 'and stop worrying.'

As it was it still didn't turn out the way Hannah might have expected.

On the night the disgraced Sarah was thrown out to fend for herself, Edith found her huddled, in a near hysterical condition, down the back alley.

For the best, the older sister decided that the only course open to them both was to seek refuge with Aunt Alice. Being certain that they would find help there.

Alice welcomed her night callers with open arms, then listened with sympathy and understanding as Edith recited the events of the evening. Clucking, tutting and cursing Harry to hell, Alice vowed that come what may, the girls would be much better off under her wing. Having waited years for the chance to really show Harry, she was delighted to be able to do anything which might increase his vexation.

Alice felt that any shame or disgrace brought into the family by Sarah, was of little consequence when compared with the ways of Harry over the years. The poor child's undoings paled significantly when measured against his. So Alice took immense pleasure from the decision to house her nieces.

She assured Hannah tat all would be well and not to worry. Even going so far as to proceed with wedding arrangements without consulting either Hannah or Harry. For the sake of decency, Sarah had to wed hastily, in order to preserve some of her dignity. The wagging tongues had more than enough to keep them busy without giving them extra fuel.

So it was, with a courage he didn't possess, the weedy Fred Ball tapped cautiously at the door in Higher Wood Street. Quaking, his innards tied in knots at the thought of facing Harry Shaw, Fred was reluctantly invited to the house.

'You've a visitor' Hannah said, showing the pale young lad in, to face Harry.

'I should have your bloody guts!' Harry barked, not looking up - and knowing full well the lad was here to formally ask for his daughter's hand. 'Out with it.'

Fred, whiter than a sheet, dragged off his cap and trembling violently, tried to stand stock still. In his near terrified state, it was an impossibility. His knees knocked shamefully.

Hannah smiled at him, a smile conveying as much warmth and encouragement as she could muster.

'I...I...' the words stuck in Fred's throat; his stomach churned alarmingly.

'By God' Harry brought his eyes up to see the quivering wreck before him 'what the hell are you?'

Fred cast his eyes nervously in Hannah's direction, then gulping desperately, began again.

'Sir, I...I...'

'Stop your dithering. Bloody Fool' Harry bellowed. 'Say what you've come to say, then get out.'

'P...p...please sir' Fred gulped once more, his stomach rising to his throat, then knowing, without doubt, he was about to shame himself, rapidly slapped his cap across his mouth – then heaved violently.

Hannah rushed forwards in an effort to guide him towards the slop stone. But it was too late. The lad's cap was full to the brim with vomit.

'You dirty, filthy bastard' Harry yelled, rising from his chair, ready to strike out.

'No Harry!' Hannah said, sharply. 'Can't you see, he's sick.'

'He'll be more than bloody sick when I've finished with him' Harry snarled. Shaking his balled fists in the air 'bringing disgrace on this family then puking all over my house.'

'Leave him, Harry, the lad's scared witless' Hannah said, taking the nauseating cap from Fred and dropping it into the sink.

'Tell him he can wed our Sarah and have done with it.

Just tell him. Can't you see he's incapable of asking?' she said.

'Nay, lass. He can ask' Harry remained firm on the issue as Hannah rinsed away the vomit. 'Don't care if he's puking all night, he can still ask.'

She sighed heavily, then squeezing the excess water from the flat cap, handed it back to Fred, saying 'go on, you'd best be sharp lad before he shows his temper.'

'Aye,' Harry growled 'I shall not wait much longer.'

Fred looked to Hannah, then amidst mumbling, and shaking, nervously managed to ask for Sara's hand.

Harry eyed him for several moments, quietly weighing the lad up and down, increasing Fred's nervousness before finally giving his answer.

Fred allowed himself a little smile, suddenly feeling proud, then quickly offered his hand.

Harry hesitated. Then as Fred was on the brink of withdrawing, he took it in his and shook it before saying 'now get out and I don't ever want to see either of you in this house again. I've given my permission for this farce of a wedding and that's all. It doesn't make things right.'

1900

Edith's day at the mill at seemed unusually long. What with a couple of young girls having to be taught the joys of cotton – one picking it up easy enough and the other completely hopeless – the going had been tough.

The heat in the Albany itself didn't help much either. It had taken hours before the lasses had grown a little accustomed to the stifling atmosphere, and the sweat that ran in rivulets down their backs. Edith knew it was the money that kept them all sweating it out; those determined not to be put off by the hard work. In fact, since the beginnings of King Cotton in Middleton, it seemed as if the whole population of the town was occupied at the mills in one way or another.

Sitting quietly by the fire, Edith reflected on the day. Her thoughts filled with people she knew, whose homes were ruled by cotton. At one time it had been weaving, mainly done in the home but now done in sweatshops.

She glanced down at the bible that lay open on her lap. She instinctively ran her fingers gently along its leather bound edges. It was her most treasured possession, a great source of comfort to her. The only thing in life that could catch her undivided attention.

Many an hour had she spent, deep in its pages.

Sighing tiredly, Edith glanced up at her mother and for a moment their eyes held each other's gaze. She noted how tired Hannah was looking these days but didn't speak as the older woman tuned her attention back to her sewing. Edith hated the change that had occurred in her mother. Hated the reason why.

From being a clean and well-dressed figure of the community, Hannah's appearance had declined dramatically. There were days when the older woman didn't even bother to dress her hair. But so far this neglect of herself had not spilled over to the children. Edith knew in her heart that, no matter what, Hannah would never neglect her children or her home, even though all thoughts for herself appeared non-existent.

Hannah's eyes began to close, her jaw gaped open awkwardly. And her fingers still clasped the dress that she was making for Elizabeth, as she dropped off into a doze.

Edith rose from her chair, placed the bible on the table, then gently, so as not to disturb Hannah, removed the dress from her mother's fingers. She would get on with some of the sewing for a while, at least until Hannah was rested.

She often had the unnerving feeling that her mother might just drop off to sleep one day, and never wake up. In her own mind, she was not quite sure how she would cope if indeed that was to happen. Her thoughts centred on the prospects of Harry becoming the burden she must carry. He would, without doubt, make life unpleasant for everyone. More so, than he did now. She nurtured the secret hope that her father would get so drunk as to not find his way home. An impossibility, she knew – the man always knew exactly which way was home – much to her disappointment.

He disgusted Edith all the time. He was filthy, unkempt, and always stunk of beer and stale tobacco. She couldn't remember when she'd last seen the man have a wash. He was her greatest source of shame and embarrassment. And she was sure the Lord would forgive all her unchristian and uncharitable thoughts about him.

'Heck' she murmured to herself as she looked up and saw him coming in the back yard. He was staggering as pushed open the door of the privy.

Hurriedly Edith vacated his chair and continued at the table, with the sewing in her hands. If he so much as caught her anywhere near the chair, she'd be in trouble.

Noisily he clattered in the door, swaying, and grinning oafishly as he lurched to stand in front of the fire. Blocking all the heat off with his frame, Edith could smell the odorous stick rise from him, as the fire warmed him up.

'He'd even smell if we burnt him' Edith mumbled to

herself, hoping he didn't hear, not looking at him at all.

'Where's my tea?' Harry asked, his words slurred, his body swaying.

'Still in the pan' Edith answered then, looking up from the sewing, added 'you should have come home sooner.'

'Don't give me any of your lip' Harry mumbled, flopping drunkenly into his chair, content now that his back was warmed through.

'Tea is tea-time. Tis way past nine o'clock and you shouldn't expect it now. Edith averted her eyes from his. Even drunk, the searching blue of his eyes was quite unnerving.

'I 'spect anything I want' he raised his voice now.

'Aye, and you get it too' she said, begrudgingly, as she put the sewing to one side and rose to attend to the pan, which was standing in the hearth.

'She asleep?' Harry questioned, his foot roughly kicking Hannah's. She jerked, waking suddenly, and drew her feet further away from his clogs.

'You didn't need to waken her' Edith reprimanded.

'She should be awake when I come home – should always be ready and waiting for Harry' he grinned, then chuckled at some amusing thought that crossed his mind.

'I'll get his tea' Hannah said, wide awake now.

'You stay where you are, mother. I'll see to it.' Edith smiled at her.

'Nay lass' Harry caught hold of Edith by the arm 'your mother will do it.'

''Tis done now' Edith shrugged him off her 'leave her be.'

'You dare speak to me like that!' Harry shouted.

'Can't you see, mother is tired. Things are getting to be too much for her, and you don't help matters' Edith faced him squarely, hoping to appeal to the better side of his nature. Not that she was sure there was a better side. 'Can't you see she's won out and you've caused it.'

'I've done nowt.'

'You have. Just look at her' Edith's anger began to rise 'she didn't look like this, years ago.'

'Edith, leave it be' Hannah spoke wearily.

'No, I won't. Things need to be said. They've needed to be said for ages, so I'll say them. He comes and goes as he pleases, and you have to answer to his beck and call, like a dog. Except dogs getter better treated. He's killing you, mother.'

'Mind your bloody tongue, lass' Harry shouted 'your Sunday school ways and nonsense will get you into trouble. Be off to bed where you belong. Tis well past the hour.'

'I've been helping mother with some of this sewing' Edith said, in defence of the late hours she was keeping. Thankful he hadn't hit her. No-one dared have any sort of angry outburst when Harry was around, at least not without inviting a sharp clout.

'Your mother doesn't need any help. Now get up them stairs or I will crack you one lady' Harry's eyes closed as he spoke, his head lolling backwards to rest on the chairback.

Hannah looked to Edith, then nodded in agreement to save any more argument.

Edith kissed her mother goodnight, then whispered low as she bent over the older woman 'you sure you'll be alright?'

'Aye, go on up lass. We shan't be long after you' Hannah smiled wearily at her daughter 'and if he drops off, he'll stay where he is.'

'Night then' Edith said lightly, then directing her voice at Harry, added 'night father.'

Harry grunted in answer at the girl he despised. At the 'holier than thou' madam he loved to hate.

oOo

Harry woke sometime in the night. His mouth was very dry. He felt cold and stiff. The fire was now just burning embers and the room was dark.

'Hannah' he spoke, hearing only his own voice in the still of the night and wincing at the throbbing tearing through his head.

No answer came and as his eyes slowly began to focus in the gloom, he sensed that he was not alone.

Realising that nature was calling, but his movements were impeded, he found himself inexplicably held fast.

Allowing a few extra moments for his tired brain to bring him from the time betwixt sleep and fully awake, he tried desperately to work out what was wrong with him.

The sudden thought that he may have had some sort of seizure or paralysis was an anxious one, bringing him out in a cold sweat. The relief poured through him when slowly he understood that his movable limbs could actually move. Albeit in a restricted way.

There was no apparent pain in his body, except for a tightness across his chest. Without panic, Harry tried to work out why it was restraint from outside and not inside.

'What the hell?' he muttered angrily. Upon trying to move his legs, they moved as one. Looking down as much as whatever was holding him would allow, he saw why. His ankles were bound.

'Buggers!' he bellowed, straining violently against the ties on his wrists. 'I'll kill the buggers.'

'I wouldn't shout if I were you' Edith's voice, quiet and soft, came to him from the darkness. 'Shouting won't get you out of that mess.'

'Undo these things now' Harry hissed. Twisting roughly to where her voice came from. 'I'll bloody well kill you when I get hold of you.'

'I don't think so' she was smiling in the gloom, he could sense 'because the more you struggle and shout, the longer you'll stay there. Besides, even a good hiding is worth seeing this.'

'Get me out of these, now' Harry struggled again, rocking his chair viciously.

'No.'

'Edith.'

'No.'

'I shall just pee where I'm sat then.'

'Go ahead' Edith said, uncaring, but nevertheless disgusted 'but you'll be sitting in it. And 'tis your chair that'll be wet.'

'Edith, I need to pee' he hissed savagely.

'I heard you the first time.'

'Bitch' his hands were beginning to feel numb through straining at the bonds. His anger was rising by the second. 'Get 'em off.'

'Calm down father' she spoke from the shadows 'you'll only tighten them knots more, and then no-one will be able to undo them.'

From the moment she'd tied him into the chair, and all the while he'd been sleeping, Edith had felt a courage she couldn't explain. Seeing him, totally helpless and vulnerable, she had enjoyed the spectacle without thinking of the consequences at all.

'You'd best undo them before I bellow loud enough to bring the whole street in here' his voice suddenly more determined, edged with a violence that struck fear within her 'now, lass, and be damned quick about it.'

Edith trembled, partly from the cold and partly from sudden fear. She stepped gingerly into his direct line of vision.

'I only did it for mother' she said apologetically, kneeling to pull at the knot the twisted linen binding his ankles together 'so she could get a good night.'

'Get my hands loose' he snarled, as he felt his feet fall free of each other.

She quickly did as he bid but was not prepared for the savage grab that caught her hair in one hand and the stinging blow from the other hand. Dragging her face close to his, she felt spittle spray her skin. His beery breath filled her nostrils as he spoke.

'You ever do that again and I'll have a mind to give you

a real good tanning.'

Edith squeaked in pain as he took her head by the hair and slapped her for what seemed an interminable length of time, before roughly pushing her to the floor.

She lay there, quite still; her face smarting, afraid to move. Afraid to breathe as he freed himself completely.

Harry stood up, stretched himself to get the circulation going again, and then as if he's forgotten Edith was there began to fumble with his flies.

'You'd best be up to bed before my temper gets the better of me' he said tiredly. The truth was his head was pounding, he needed to relieve himself and he didn't want to bother with Edith at this time of the night.

Shaking, Edith lifted herself from the floor and began to back out of the room, thankful she hadn't been hit more than she had.

'Urgh!' An involuntary sound of disgust escaped from her lips. The sound of hissing as he urinated into the dying embers of the fire made her feel only contempt for the man.

'You left it too late for me to pee anywhere else, lass' Harry said, his harsh laughter following her up the stairs as she rushed off in utter disgust.

'I'm off out for a time' young Harry said, wrapping his scarf around his neck and donning his flat cap 'you'll have some peace and quiet.'

'Aye, I will' Hannah sighed, tired. The girls had taken John with them to a church meeting in the New Jerusalem; the rest were up in bed. 'But mind you're home when the Nowster's stopped.'

'I'm always home' young Harry smiled. His Mum always said that, like all the other mothers did, The Nowster was the signal for all those out and about of an evening to be off home. And woe betides those who weren't home when it finished ringing at ten of the clock. No excuses were tolerated because the single bell in the Parish Church could be heard all over Middleton. It rung for ten minutes to give the young ones plenty of time to reach home. Young Harry, often had to put on an extra spurt and sprint up Wood Street. But he always made it – sometimes just getting to the door as the bell faded into silence.

'Ah well – mind how you go' she called after him as he disappeared through the door 'and no bringing any troubles back with you.'

He was a decent lad, she mused; quiet, hardworking, and no bother. Not a bit like his father. Chalk and cheese, they were.

Putting down the dishcloth she'd finished knitting, Hannah gave her attention to a pile of collars in dire need of turning. Reaching for her needle and thread, thoughts suddenly centred on Harry, and she automatically sniffed the air.

'Ah, 'tis doing nicely' she mumbled to herself, quite content with the charred smell filling the room 'and it'll serve him right.'

Harry had not been home again for a few days. She expected him tonight. Having wages in his pocket, he'd be home if only to toss some coppers her way. But after what she'd done, and when he found out, Hannah couldn't be sure she'd get any brass out of him. Mind you, he still got his dinners regular – as regular as night followed day. She saw to that, always. The childer took it in turns to take his dinner to work when they came home from school for theirs. It wasn't something he'd had to do without, even when he wasn't home for days on end. She sent messages to him, through the childer, and in turn, would ask how their father was keeping. So, she deserved some coppers at least.

Having only done a couple of collars, Hannah heard him come in the yard. Non-plussed she carried on with the task in hand, knowing he'd most likely go into the privy first. Her inners began to churn, anticipating what could happen. She wasn't feared. Not exactly. More on the edgy side.

Harry shuffled in to stand by the fire. Clearing his throat noisily, he spat forcefully into the flames. The red hot coals sizzled and hissed as they swallowed his offerings. Turning to warm his back, Harry watched at her.

Hannah could sense him looking, could feel his eyes on her. She continued to sew, determined not to acknowledge his presence. It was something she could well do without.

Presently he sat in his chair, with much shuffling and coughing and general nuisance, and said jovially 'I'm home.'

'So I heard' Hannah spoke then, but didn't look up from her needlework. She was about to try his patience and was more than willing to see how far she could go.

'I said, I'm home' he repeated with agitation.

'Umm, I heard.'

'Well?' he questioned, his voice rising.

'Well, what?'

'Where's my tea?' he began to drum his fingers on the arm of the chair.

'In the pot' Hannah raised her eyes, just enough to peer

over her nose at him. Out of curiosity, she had to see his face. Had to read what was on his mind.

'You'd best put that little lot down then' he motioned at the sewing in her lap 'and get my tea out.'

Deliberately taking her time, Hannah rose from the chair, dropping the collars behind her onto the vacant seat. Reaching for the cloth hanging on the line just below the mantelpiece, she heard him clear his throat again, in an attempt to make her hurry.

She tipped the contents of the pot onto a plate and set it down on the table saying 'there. 'Tis out' before quickly returning to sit down.

'What the bloody hell do you call that?' he exploded, his eyes seeing only the charred remains of something disgusting.

'It's your tea' she commented innocently.

'I'm not bloody well having that' he swiped the plate from the table, sending it crashing to the floor 'get me something decent.'

'It were a good dinner three days ago, so I thought I'd best keep it for you.' Hannah spoke very calmly, knowing that all hell was about to let loose.

'I want something proper, and I want it now' he bellowed, moving so close she could feel his stale breath on her face.

'There's nowt else' she said in as strong a voice as possible.

He hit her then.

The sharp blow caught her about the head and, for a moment, Hannah could've sworn she saw coloured stars dancing before her eyes. The pain shot through her from ear to ear as she sat there, unmoving.

'Bitch!' Harry raged. 'Slovenly bitch!'

She didn't utter a word. With head bowed, Hannah tried to blot out everything happening around her, not daring to move an inch.

Her apparent ignorance of his needs incensed him

further. He kicked out at savagely the mess on the flagstones, sending the lot flying into the fender around the hearth.

'Now get my tea!' Harry shouted, sure she would comply.

''Tis on the floor' Hannah muttered, her nerves now at breaking point.

'By God, woman' he caught hold of her hair and yanked her from the chair in a frenzy of rage. 'You'll get me some tea or I'll make you pay for this - good and proper.'

Hannah's hands flew to her head in an effort to take some of the strain from him pulling her hair. 'You'll do it now!' he thundered, flinging her towards the oven.

Putting out her hand to steady herself as she careered forwards, she felt the instant pain as her hand came into contact with the red hot fire surround. Drawing back in pain, she instinctively cried out, holding the injured hand to her middle.

'You make me bloody sick' Harry raged. Ignoring her pain, he lunged again 'you lazy, slovenly, good for nothing. Get up them stairs and don't dare come down again.'

He pushed her towards the stairs. Hannah, hurting from the burn, hurting from his anger, stubbornly refused to show him any tears. This time, with fierce determination, she wasn't going to let him see how much he could upset her. This time, she was going to be as strong as possible, no matter what he did or said to her. The satisfaction would be hers – not his.

'Get up them bloody stairs' he bellowed. Pushing her with great force 'and stay up there, till I tell you different. I'll learn you. As quick as hell, I'll learn you.'

Quickly she climbed up, glad to be out of his way. Knowing that when confined to the bedroom he wouldn't bother her again.

'And you'll be getting no coppers off me this day' he shouted up after her, content now she was cowed and subdued.

'I'm master in this house' he mumbled as if the need to convince himself of the fact was of utmost importance.

Then louder, repeating himself, he added 'I'm master in this house. Too bloody right I am.'

Hannah, nursing her wounds in the quiet of the bedroom, could hear him. But it worried her not. He'd shout and rage for a while longer, that much she knew. Then all would be calm.

Taking comfort from the security and peace of the isolation in the warmth of the dark room, lit only be the firelight glow, she felt at ease.

Content that, for once, she'd had her way.

1905

'Have you spoken with your mother?' Harry leaned heavily against the bar in the Dusty Miller, slurring his words in John's direction.

'Nay' John answered, greedily downing ale faster than it could be drawn 'I've only thought on asking you.'

'Hah!' Harry mocked his son 'tis the ale talking, lad. When you've slept on it a while, you'll maybe change your ideas. Full of horse muck you are. Fancy notions that'll never amount to ought. Any road, what's wrong with staying where you were born and bred; amongst your own sort?'

John looked his father up and down and saw through eyes clouded by smoke and ale, the image of what he, himself, could become. And the thought was depressing. Enough to evoke anger and defiance within him.

His father lolled drunkenly before him. Dirty – nay filthy – in his stinking frock coat. No pride in his appearance whatsoever, and caring nought for anyone but himself and his constant alehouse visits. The man had drifted aimlessly, down the years. Content with nothing.

John could only evaluate his father's life as a mess. Of it always having been a mess. And forever, into the foreseeable future, being exactly the same.

He sure as hell didn't want the same drudgery for himself. John wasn't sure what he wanted, but he knew, without a doubt, his life was not going to be a mirror image of his father's. Not the same mind numbing daily grind. Anything but that.

A future away from the dark satanic mills was his dream.

He dreamed. During the day he dreamed. Throughout the night, while others slept soundly in their beds, John dreamed. Dreamed of what he could be. The ideas formed in his head, until he felt that all he had to do was reach out and touch his dreams to make it work. Then, escape would be his.

'Nay, father' John answered, looking Harry straight in the eyes "tis not the ale. My minds made up. I shall go to London first, then a ship, when I've enough brass to take me to the other side of the world.'

'You're bloody touched lad' Harry sneered, disbelieving. 'Should be in a bloody lunatic asylum. Fancy ideas – humph – daft bugger.'

'I want more than you've got' John protested loudly 'much more. I won't be satisfied with anything less.'

'I've got all I need' Harry grinned smugly, slightly amused by his son's outburst.

'Ah, you've got nowt' John sighed. 'Nowt at all.'

'Nay, and you'll have nowt either' Harry slapped his hand down heavily on John's shoulder. 'Stay put lad. You've got work and a good home. What more is there? Traipsing off all over the show isn't for working folks. Find yourself a lass and be content with that.'

"Tis not enough' John mumbled. Shrugging Harry's arm off. 'I want to be certain of work. Short time or stopped is no good. I can't live like that. Can't be content with never knowing if there'll even be work on the morrow or not.'

'We're an old Middleton family, born and bred. Been here for donkey's years we have' Harry began to rant. 'Born and bred to work all our lives for what little we can get. Your grandfather and his grandfather before him all stayed put. There was no buggering off. My God they saw some hard times. Times you know nowt about. But they still stayed here where they belonged. Same as you will.'

Harry was swaying a little as he spoke. John couldn't be sure whether the words were coming from his father's heart or because of the enormous amount of ale in his belly. 'Edward's not gone and neither has our Harry. What makes you so damned different?'

'I've told you. Now let it drop.' John didn't wish to pursue the matter any further, now that a hush had descended on the bar, all eyes and ears now strained in their direction. His mind was decided. No amount of talking or words of apparent drunken wisdom would sway the way he felt.

'I shan't' Harry bellowed, totally unaware of his collected audience. 'Heed your father. Lad. You'll see I'm right. Why, you've never been further than Manchester – and you even had to hold your mother's hand then.'

'I don't want to be stuck in this hole forever. What is there for me?' John thumped the bar in frustration. Then turning to face those watching, angrily he included all and sundry within earshot.

'Cotton mills or dyeworks, when there's work, then the alehouse. I won't have a life like yours forever and ever. Look at yourselves. Just have a bloody good look. There's not one of you got two ha'pennies to rub together, even after all the hours you sweat for your brass. Working class, you might be, but poor working class at that. Well, I'll not have that.'

Someone laughed. A few muttered. Others sniggered behind their ale.

'Eh Harry' a voice loud and insistent, with a hint of amusement, rang loud and clear 'give him a bloody good hiding. He wants putting in his place, the soft bugger.'

'Ah, go on with you, getting all het up' Harry drew on his pipe, ignoring the remark. Turning to John in a way for all to hear he said 'Bugger off. Go and find what it is you'll be wanting. You'll rue the day. And I'll wager we'll be seeing you back here afore too long.'

John's face brightened of a sudden and his spirits lifted somewhat. Although now of full age, he felt it necessary to have approval from his father in one form or another. Whether his father was approving as such didn't matter.

Harry had told him to go ahead, and that's exactly what he intended to do.

1914

40

She'd been lying in bed for days now and it wasn't like Hannah. Always up and around. Busy from dawn to dusk and beyond, she knew instinctively that she might not be up and doing again.

Edith, alarmed by her mother's grave condition, had gone to fetch the doctor. The very act itself struck a note of fear in Hannah, as sick as she was. She'd never had the doctor. Never had any situation in the family when such serious matters were called for. She half-hoped her daughter was caught up in some blind panic.

Hannah couldn't remember the day when she'd first felt less than well. Because tiredness, through the years, had steadily crept up on her, until she felt constantly weary. She dismissed the feeling of tightness in her chest as nothing more than the usual winter chill. Ignored the resultant persistent cough which tore painfully through her. The morning dawned when trying to clamber from her bed she fell back on it. Her strength having disappeared. Her limbs without energy.

Elizabeth, the youngest, found her mother having taken bad, and full of concern and overwhelming love, tended Hannah immediately. Tucking the sick woman into bed, with firm orders to stay put. Elizabeth shouted for Thomas to come and get life into the fire, while she went to fetch Edith and Aunt Alice.

The older women arrived in double quick time. Alarmed and concerned, they ministered to Hannah, making her as comfortable as possible. The while clucking with disapproval at her having let herself become so poorly.

Edith decided she would stay. Someone capable to have available to tend Hannah night and day. If Harry should come home, it was better Edith be there, rather than Aunt Alice. If Alice had his way it'd be neither of them. But Edith cared nought for what he might want. Her mother needed her.

Hannah, too weak to move, lay back on the pillow. Her body exhausted, her mind wandering to the past, recalling the good times and the bad, as delirium swept over her.

A faint smile formed on her lips as she remembered Harry, from days so long ago. The ever so bold young man – arrogant – in fact, plain downright cocksure. With his cheeky smile, he'd made her heart beat faster, entrancing the impressionable seventeen your old with his warm charming ways. She could picture the canal bank up at Mills Hill. The miles they had walked, arm in arm, through sunshine and rain, up to Slattocks and back. She could almost feel the shade of the trees in Alkrington Woods as they took refuge from the heat of the sun, their eyes for each other only.

Hannah tossed uncomfortably in her bed, as pleasanter times and idyllic memories became entangled with the harsher side of Harry Shaw. His women, young Harry, the beatings, and his drunken ways. She'd learnt the folly of youth alright. Paid with her lifetime for the mistake of loving Harry and believing a man could change.

She'd realised it too late. He belonged to no-one but himself. There had been times, very few she knew, when he'd come close to giving her his all. But on reflection, Hannah hadn't really scratched the surface. The man could spread himself around. Everyone could sample a bit of him. But the whole man? Never.

Hannah began to shiver. The room was warm and cosy but she suddenly felt extremely cold as the memories flooded through her.

It was a torture of the worse kind, bringing to mind the episodes she assumed were well forgotten. The times when, drunk beyond all reason, Harry had made excessive demands on her weary body. The endless years of bearing his children and the unforeseen blessings of countless miscarriages. All part of her wedded duty. They had wrecked her completely. It was with a mix of feelings that she viewed his association with the woman from Little Park. On the one hand, it bought shame and disgrace on the family name. But the longer he stayed with his fancy woman, the less Hannah had to suffer his anger and demands.

Her delirious thoughts switched to her children. Her furrowed brow relaxed somewhat, as Edward came to mind. Born at a time when she still loved Harry above all else, the lad had never caused her a moment's worry. Edward, she felt, had chosen well in marrying Agnes. They made a lovely family. Her one concern in that direction was that both of them enjoyed partaking of ale – and with six children to keep, Hannah sometimes wondered at the wisdom of their actions.

Edith, she always assumed, would have remained a spinster, like her Aunts, Alice and Beth. But much to Hannah's surprise, she had found herself a wonderful man in Jack. Although well over full age, she had taken plenty of time before committing herself to marriage. Hannah knew why. She had seen all the bad times at home, had always blamed her father while remaining an absolute comfort to her mother. So, it was with utter caution she courted and wed. Hannah recalled the night when Edith had been thrown out by Harry for her defence of her sister, and how both of them had gone to live with Alice. It had taken much persuasion before Harry would allow Edith back into the family home.

But he had done, under extreme protest.

Harry sprung to mind again then, and the way in which he had brought the news of young Harry to her. Ah, she thought. Young Harry was a lovely child. Not hers, but an obvious credit to her now. He didn't know she wasn't his mother and, as long as Hannah had her way, he would never be told. He lived in Back Kid Street now, with his sickly wife Ann and their three children.

Ah, Sarah and Fred. Hannah felt a tear prick her eyes as the heartache of Sarah's departure from home tore at her heart, all over again. The poor child, banished by Harry, met Fred Ball. A quick wedding for the sake of decency was the way it was. The pair, living with Alice, until the birth of the twins. Then with luck at someone's misfortune, they got a house on Oldham Road. Hannah's brow creased again as she wondered why they had never had more children.

Harry had never spoken to Sarah again, a thought that brought more salty tears streaming down Hannah's face.

'Oh God, will he ever forgive her?' she cried silently in her own private agony. Praying fervently that her family could be together without anger and accusations.

Even John's setting off for the other side of the world had caused ructions and derision from Harry. Scoffing at the lad's ideas. Harry washed his hands of the business.

Hannah, more flexible, had wished John well. Holding back the heartache as he went, her care reaped rewards upon receiving letters telling of all the places Hannah had only ever read about. Her great joy was when John reached Australia, settling in New South Wales, and sending word that he would soon be getting married. Her one regret now was knowing she would never see him again. Never see his wife. Never see the family he would have.

Hannah cried. The sound, heart rending, in the peace of the bedroom.

'And Thomas...oh, Thomas' she wept, mumbling. Knowing of his ideas and leanings towards the army. One of his friends had been in the territorials for some time now, and she was sure that wonderous tales had filled her son's head. Fighting and the possibility of having to kill another human being was surely not what her Thomas craved? He hadn't been brought up that way.

'What is it, mother?'

Hannah realised Edith was hovering around the bed.

'Are you back?' she whispered weakly; her thoughts broken of a sudden.

'Yes, mother. How do you feel now?' Edith felt

Hannah's forehead and gazed down at the mother with utter concern 'why are you weeping?'

''Tis the pain love, just the pain.'

'The doctor will be here soon' Edith spoke gently 'and Edward's gone to find father.'

'Will he come?' Hannah's eyes began to close.

'He'd better' Edith squeezed her mother's hand, willing the sick woman to keep going, at all costs.

'You'll manage without me.'

'Don't, mother, please. You're not leaving us'

Edith straightened the sheets. Tucking them comfortably around Hannah as she dozed fitfully. Then bending, she kissed her mother lightly on the cheek before reluctantly leaving to go downstairs.

'Oh, you found him then?' Edith spoke sharply as Edward and Harry came through the door.

'Aye' Edward answered, glancing sideways at his father.

'Which was it this time, the Dusty or that woman?' Edith stood solid as a rock, her arms crossed about her chest, her person immovable.

'Edith!' Edward admonished 'leave it be.'

Harry brushed past his daughter and sank into his chair without speaking.

'Can you believe him?' Edith was asking Edward as she followed her father into the kitchen 'and he's disgustingly filthy.'

'Leave it alone.' Edward sat down. 'How is she?'

'Not good at all. Oh, Edward, I don't think there's anything we can do now...she's sinking quite fast.' Edith spoke accusingly, her gaze directed at Harry.

'You should go up and see her' Edward said to his father.

Harry sucked his pipe and glared at his eldest children.

'I wouldn't let him near her' his daughter said loudly 'God only knows what filth he's come from. He's not fit to be in my mother's company.'

'Edith, for God's sake' Edward angrily hoped to silence her sharp tongue, because he could guess what would happen.

'Your sister has a way with words' Harry made the statement, quite controlled as inwardly he seethed.

'You disgust me' Edith sneered, but as she turned to move away. Harry was out of the chair in an instant and had caught her by the shoulders.

'Father...' Edward stood up instinctively, ready for trouble.

'Come on Edith' Harry cajoled 'tell me what I am. Come on.'

'You're a..., you're a...' Edith was trembling as Harry's

grip on her shoulders tightened. She smelled the drink on his breath.

'Bastard?' Harry laughed. 'You can't say it can you. Dear refined daughter of mine. Because you can't cuss and swear, can you?'

'Get off me' she tried to shrug herself free of his grasp, his odour sickening her.

'Leave her father' Edward came towards them and tried to help Edith free herself, but Harry inadvertently caught him a blow to the stomach with his elbow.

'My mother is dying up there, have you no feelings?' Edith spat the words at harry, venomously.

'More than you'll ever have' Harry laughed coarsely, catching her hair in his hands and pulling her face close to his.

Edith closed her eyes to shut out the sight and smell of him, paling at his nearness.

'Come on Edith, give your old father a kiss then' Harry teased.

'Please, father, don't' Edward pleaded on Edith's behalf.

'Bugger off, lad. I'll tame her yet. If it's the last thing I do' he hissed.

Edith began to cry as Harry dragged her even closer.

'Have you ever felt a real man, this close?' he rasped.

'For God's sake, leave her alone,' Edward grabbed his father's arm, intent on putting a stop to proceedings 'this isn't doing anyone any good.'

'Shit' Harry laughed. 'She's loving it. She wants to know what your mother saw in me. And by God, I could really show her. Could show her what they all see in me.'

'Come on' Edward gently tugged at his father's arm 'mother needs you.'

Harry roughly planted a kiss of Edith's mouth, and still laughing, threw her head back until she almost toppled over backwards.

Angrily she wiped her arm across her lips, then lifted it,

as if to strike out.

'You do it, lass, you just do it' he coaxed 'and I'll bury you.'

Seeing the violence in his face, she lowered her arm and turning on her heel, sped from the house.

'There was no need for any of that,' Edwards spoke carefully, used to his father's ways.

'Come off it, lad' Harry sniggered 'she's like a dried up old maid. And it kills her. Because at my age I can still rut around.'

'You're drunk' Edward stated, blankly.

'Not really lad, not really' Harry retrieved his pipe and banged it out on the hearth 'just because I've had a few drops of ale.'

'More like a few jugs.'

'Hah, and what about you?'

'I keep it reasonable.'

'Maybe lad, maybe' Harry sighed, clamped an arm on his son's shoulder and said, 'suppose I'd best get upstairs to Hannah then.'

'It would be a good idea' Edward smiled. He still admired Harry a little. 'Er, father, before you go?'

'She might not last the night. Please be kind.'

'Don't worry, lad' he said 'don't worry. I won't hurt her anymore.'

And he meant it. For once in his life, he spoke from the heart.

'Where is he?' Jack stormed into the house, Edith tagging along behind him. Like a shadow.

'Who?' Edward asked nonchalantly.

'You know who I mean. I'll kill him if he touches Edith again.' Jack's anger was an extension to Edith's.

'Don't be so damned stupid, Jack' Edward said calmly. 'Sit down and calm yourself a bit. We don't want your carrying on now.'

'I won't' Jack stood squarely before Edward.

'Don't take it out on me' Edward smiled.

'From what Edith said, you weren't much help. Maybe I should thump you too. You know what they say, don't you? Like father like son.'

Edith took Jack by the arm, a united front.

'Go ahead if it makes you feel any better.' Edward was quite unconcerned by the weak threat 'but you'll come off worse.'

'He's sick. Absolutely sick' Jack ranted. 'Utter scum. Filth. A beast of..., of...'

'Give up Jack' Edward said 'it won't change anything. A few choice expletives might help you know. But you don't swear, do you? Another of Edith's little features.'

'I'm warning you, Edward, I'll thrash you in a minute.'

'Edith' Edward spoke to his sister 'will you shut him up. What you had to drag him here for puzzles me. Father is up there with my mother, and we'll have no more of this. Let's show some decency.'

'He should have thought about decency when he was trying to do those awful things to me' now Edith's turn to sound off.

'Horseshit Edith' Edward grinned 'he wasn't doing anything to you, and you know it.'

'He would have done if you hadn't been there' she said.

'Maybe he plays the fool because you remind him of how mother used to look when she was a young lass' her brother teased.

''Tis disgusting. And you're as bad. How Agnes puts up with you, I'll never know' Edith spoke with a rush of contempt.

'Ah now then, you'll never know' he smiles, then added, an afterthought 'take Jack home, Edith. If father should come back down, there's no telling what might happen.'

But it was too late. Harry had heard the commotion and had left Hannah's bedside to find out who was causing the noise.

'Come back for more have you lass?' Harry grinned as he spoke to Edith. 'Why've you brought him?'

'You!' Jack grabbed Harry's arm. 'You had better leave her alone. She is my wife and I'd thank you to keep your hands off her. Touch her again and I'll kill you.'

Harry was amused by Jack's forceful outburst. 'And you expect me to stand around and let you.'

Jack felt suddenly stupid. Harry wasn't an easy man to deal with, and he didn't really know how to handle him.

'I'm warning you.'

'Don't ever threaten me' Harry shrugged Jack off him, and bodily trapped him up against the wall 'and you'll do well to remember it. Now get out of my house and don't come back.'

'Your house?' Jack commented as Harry moved to allow him to go. 'You're never in it. God alone knows why you are here now.'

'Get out!' Harry bellowed as his right fist met Jack's face. 'Get out and take that excuse of a woman with you.'

Jack stumbled backwards, reeling slightly from the blow. Edith ran to him, helped him to keep his feet, and guided him towards the front door hastily.

'I'm coming back to be with my mother!' she shouted, as she slammed the front door behind her.

'Bastard' Harry swore lightly under his breath, 'bastard.'

43

She looked clean and comfortable, lay in the large bed. What stuck him immediately was her hair. Someone, probably Edith, had tidied it up, but it was the colour that drew his attention.

Hannah was decidedly grey – and he couldn't for the life of him remember having noticed before.

His own was almost silver white, and it had been for some years now, but he couldn't understand now hers had changed so rapidly.

Shuffling silently over to the bed, Harry sat on the edge closets to her. Straight backed and tense he caught hold of the hand lying on the coverlet. It was hot, more than he'd imagined, and somewhere deep inside it struck a chord of fear. He almost wanted to withdraw any contact.

He was feared alright. Always having shied away from the sick and the dying, beads of perspiration broke onto his brow as he tried to contain his own discomfort. He didn't want to be here, not now. Didn't want to be pressurised into staying and doing what he knew was only right. But something held him there. Something he didn't want to admit – not even to himself.

Hannah moved restlessly. It caused him to half-turn, surprised.

Her cheeks were and unhealthy rosy shade and her lips faintly blue as she tried to painfully whisper words that would not come.

He thought he felt an unmistakeable trace of pressure from the hand resting in his.

Harry saw the tears slide gently and silently from between her closed eyes, glistening as they caught on her lashes. Without a second thought, he carefully, so as not to disturb her, brushed away the tiny droplets with the tip of his thumb.

'I've sent for them all' he spoke low, his voice rough,

'all the young ones as well.'

Her eyes opened momentarily, the effort involved being almost too much for her to bear; then just as suddenly, they closed heavily.

Squeezing the hand, he was still holding tightly, Harry repeated his words.

Hannah knew she was dying now. She'd known for days, in those moments when her reasoning was clear. Yet she'd clung to the thoughts of being well again. All hope was lost now though. Harry's appearance now confirmed her worst fears.

She knew it had taken much effort on his part to be here and she knew why he hadn't been home since she took to her bed. But seeing him here, through glazed eyes, gladdened her tired soul. He had come. He wasn't going to let her die without being with her, and she was more than thankful for that much.

Her eyes closed again, the lids like leaden weights and she felt herself drifting off. Her mind was working as she partly dozed, going over and over all the things Harry had been and done. She could see their first meeting and their wedding, as vivid pictures of the past began to crowd her. She'd had fitful times, like now, throughout the last few days, and she'd expected anger and hatred in strong tones, with all her emotions coming to the fore. But she felt different now, as the memories flooded through. She couldn't get the right sentiments to match the pictures she was seeing in her mind. Instead, there was a strange calm. A peace she couldn't understand.

'I loved you Harry Shaw' she whispered slowly, the sudden urge to say it, overwhelming.

Harry didn't hear. His mind preoccupied with the sounds carrying up from below, as the younger ones arrived, and the adults gathered.

'I shall bring the childer up to you soon' Harry turned to her 'but I'll stay a while yet.'

There was a faint hint of a smile on her face, and he

took it to mean she was pleased.

'Hannah' he mumbled, almost choking at the thought of what he was about to say, 'I'm not much good at saying the right things. And I never was. There's not much I can do to make amends. But I want you to know' he took a deep breath, then added very quietly...

'I'm a sorry man for all I've done to you lass. I'm a rough man with rough edges. Never good enough for the likes of you. Hannah, you were the sweetest, kindest soul I ever set eyes on. Full of goodness and fine ways. I did love you and I wanted you more than ought else. But it was wrong of me to take things too far. We shouldn't have wed at all. I brought my bad ways to you because I couldn't live with your fine ways...but I weren't to know. Oh God, Hannah, I weren't to know...'

He took another deep breath. sensing dampness about his eyes. He'd never said anything like that to anyone. He never admitted his mistakes. Not even to himself. But now he'd done it. His palms were sweating badly, and he felt a little shaky, but he'd done it.

He leaned forward to kiss her forehead. Her smile was still there, firmly fixed.

Hannah hadn't heard a word.

She was far beyond hearing anything he might ever say again. Far beyond being hurt by Harry Shaw – ever.

'Hannah' he mumbled. Horrified, he dropped her lifeless hand. Quickly he backed away from the bed.

Quaking, and breathing rapidly, his eyes never leaving her face, he stood petrified. He prayed that no-one would deign to come upstairs at this moment. He needed time to compose himself. Time to get over the initial shock and sudden panic.

He'd be finished as a man if any of them saw him like this. Vulnerable and weak.

He stood there for what seemed like an age until he felt himself capable and more presentable. Until the shaking had ceased. Once more he felt in control within himself.

When they heard his tread on the stairs, they knew. Harry had no need for words. They knew.

Edith began to cry, noisily and unashamedly, then rushed wildly at the stairs.

Harry put his arms out to stop her 'Nay lass, wait awhile.'

Then scooping the grandchildren to him in a single motion, he said wearily, as if the life had gone from him too

'C'mon, let's go up. I want you all to say 'night 'night to nana.'

oOo

ACKNOWLEDGMENTS

I began writing this novel almost thirty years ago. A work of fiction, inspired by stories of a town I grew up in. A novel which has lain, unpublished, for all that time.

I owe much to my daughter, Marie, whose encouragement has helped me to finally bring it to life. Through her patience and a good many hours work she has turned my old typed manuscript to a modern day electronic and printed book.

And a huge thank you to Steve Whitworth of Steve Whitworth Arts for creating the fabulous artwork for the book cover and reference map.

Mags Fletcher, 2020

ABOUT THE AUTHOR

Mags Fletcher was born in Middleton near Manchester in the 1940s. Brought up and educated in this old mill town, she is a proud Mum to a daughter and two sons, and a doting nana.

She is recognised as the family historian and avid genealogist, with a love of the social history of her hometown of Middleton, which inspired the idea for this, her first book.

Printed in Great Britain
by Amazon